POWER BASICS ®

Biology

Teacher's Guide

WALCH  PUBLISHING

1   2   3   4   5   6   7   8   9   10

ISBN 0-8251-5619-X

Table of Contents

Power Basics®

READING LEVEL 4

INTEREST LEVEL 6-12

Power Basics® Science

Power Up Your Basic Skills Curriculum!

These practical books provide the essentials of the science curriculum: Earth and space science, biology, chemistry, and physics. In each book, learners build literacy and critical-thinking skills that enable them to interpret, evaluate, analyze, and synthesize scientific information — and apply these skills in their daily lives. With manageable step-by-step lessons, clearly defined examples, controlled vocabulary support, and frequent practice and review, your students will gain confidence in what they are learning.

Power Basics on-level content and below-level readability pack a powerful punch!

Power Basics® Earth and Space Science
Second Edition

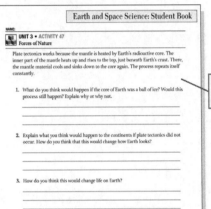

4 New Programs!

Workbook activities offer practice and reinforcement.

Lessons provide clear learning goals for students.

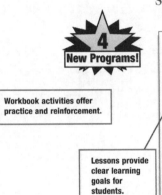

Power Basics® Earth and Space Science
Second Edition

Send students' interest in science skyrocketing!

- Explores the origins of the universe and focuses on celestial bodies including the Sun, the Moon, planets, and stars
- Covers space and all Earth's systems, including the lithosphere, the atmosphere, and the hydrosphere
- Reaches all students with captivating, on-level content with a below-level readability
- Meets National Science Education Standards
- Helps students prepare for standardized testing
- Includes timely material

Power Basics® Biology Second Edition

Get to the heart of learning about living organisms!

- Explores the six kingdoms of life, human anatomy, and cell biology
- Dissects the dynamics of living systems, including evolution, ecosystems, the structure of organisms, and the functions of living things
- Reaches all students with high-interest content at a low reading level
- Meets National Science Education Standards
- Helps students prepare for standardized testing

Power Basics® Physics Second Edition

Make physics a positive force in your classroom!

- Covers force and motion, light, electricity and magnetism, and energy and heat
- Includes modern physics, including particle physics and relativity
- Reaches all high school students with captivating, low-reading-level text
- Meets National Science Educational Standards
- Helps students prepare for standardized testing

Power Basics® Chemistry Second Edition

Help students get a charge out of learning!

- Introduces the periodic table and explains its importance
- Covers all areas of chemistry, including matter and measurement, atoms, molecules, and types of chemical reactions
- Motivates students to learn and follow the scientific method
- Meets National Science Education Standards
- Helps students prepare for standardized testing

Content adheres to the NSE standards!

READING
LEVEL
4

INTEREST
LEVEL
6-12

Physics: Student Book

LESSON 2: Dynamics

GOAL: To understand Newton's Laws of Motion; to use these laws to explain why things move the way they do

WORDS TO KNOW

centripetal   perpendicular
friction   principle of inertia
net force   reaction
newton   rotational inertia
normal force   torque

Newton's First Law and Inertia

The ancient Greek scientists believed that the natural state of all objects was to be still, or not moving. For example, a ball will not roll unless it is pushed. If you roll the ball across a carpet, it slows down and stops. It won't start moving again until somebody pushes it.

However, in the 1600s, the English scientist Isaac Newton realized that there is actually a force making the ball stop—friction. If you roll the ball on a smooth floor, it will roll much farther before stopping than it would on a carpeted floor or other rough surface. If you could completely eliminate friction, the ball could roll forever. This led to Newton's first law of motion, the principle known as inertia.

Look at the two diagrams below. If the woman does not push the cart, will it move by itself? Of course not. What will happen

> "Words to Know" provides controlled vocabulary support for students.

★ SUPPORTS ★
NO CHILD LEFT BEHIND

Power Basics® Physics
Second Edition

Physics: Workbook

NAME:

UNIT 1 • ACTIVITY 1
Translation and Vectors

Distance and displacement are two quantities that may seem to mean the same thing, yet have different definitions and meanings.

Distance is a scalar quantity. It refers to how much ground an object has covered during its motion.

Displacement is a vector quantity. It refers to how far out of place an object is. In other words, it is the object's change in position.

To practice learning the difference between these two concepts, use the grid below to trace the motion of Fido taking a walk. Each square in the grid is 1 m by 1m.

Fido starts in the bottom left hand corner of the grid. Then, Fido walks 5 m north, 8 m east, 1 m north, 2 m west, and, finally, 6 m south.

In the end, what is the distance that Fido has traveled?

What is Fido's displacement?

> Workbook supports differentiation with multiple intelligence activities.

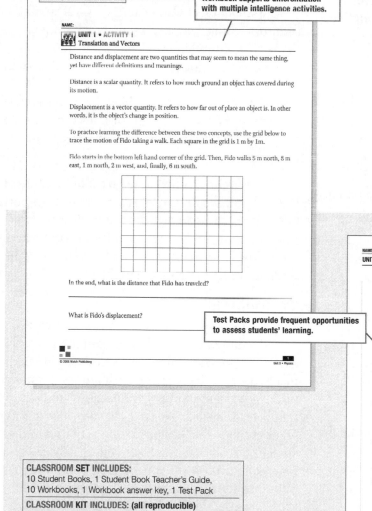

© 2005 Walch Publishing   Unit 3 • Physics

Power Basics® Chemistry
Second Edition

Power Basics® Biology Second Edition

Biology: Test Pack

NAME: DATE:

UNIT 1 • DYNAMICS OF LIFE TEST

1. All living things have.
   a. eyes   b. a heart
   c. DNA   d. the capacity for sexual reproduction

2. All living things use nutrition to make energy in a process called:
   a. respiration   b. metabolism
   c. decomposition   d. photosynthesis

3. Viruses are not considered to be alive because they lack the ability to:
   a. grow   b. metabolize
   c. excrete   d. move

4. Which of the following is not a primary function of life?
   a. reproduction   b. growth
   c. caring for offspring   d. finding nutrition

5. The basic unit for all living things is the:
   a. tissue   b. organ
   c. cell   d. system

6. An animal that is organized at the cellular level is a(n):
   a. sea anemone   b. wasp
   c. elephant   d. sponge

7. Sea stars and their relatives are _____ symmetrical.
   a. radially   b. bilaterally
   c. non   d. centrally

© 2005 Walch Publishing   Unit 1 • Biology: Test Pack

> Test Packs provide frequent opportunities to assess students' learning.

CLASSROOM SET INCLUDES:
10 Student Books, 1 Student Book Teacher's Guide,
10 Workbooks, 1 Workbook answer key, 1 Test Pack

CLASSROOM KIT INCLUDES: (all reproducible)
1 Binder, 1 Student Book, 1 Student Book Teacher's Guide,
1 Workbook, 1 Workbook answer key, 1 Test Pack

To the Teacher

Overview

Power Basics® is a complete textbook program designed to meet the needs of students who are daunted by the length and complexity of traditional textbooks. The goal of all textbook programs is to provide students with important new information. However, in traditional textbook programs, this goal is often overshadowed by other considerations. Many textbooks are written for the above-average reader and cover a wide range of content. They are filled with photographs, illustrations, and other visual elements. For some students, the amount of material is overpowering, the visual elements are distracting, and the rapid pace is unnerving. In *Power Basics®*, we revisited the basic goal, developing a streamlined textbook program that presents the essential content students need to succeed.

Program Components

As with traditional textbook programs, *Power Basics®* includes a core textbook and ancillary products designed to round out the program. The student text provides coverage of the essential content in each subject area. A consumable workbook provides a variety of activities for each lesson, including practice activities, extension activities, and activities designed for different learning styles.

Teacher support materials include a teacher's guide and test pack for each student text. The teacher's guide includes the following: an overview of each unit in the student text; suggestions for extension activities; the student text glossary and appendixes; a complete answer key to all practice activities and unit reviews in the student text; classroom record-keeping forms; and graphic organizers for student use.

For more detailed assessments, the test pack offers a pretest, unit tests for each unit in the student text, a posttest, and test-taking strategies for students.

Student Text Organization

The student text is divided into units. Each unit contains a series of lessons on related topics, with one lesson for each topic. Each lesson begins with a clear, student-centered goal and a list of key words that are introduced in the lesson. The definitions for these words are included in the glossary, which can be found in this book and at the end of the student text.

Next comes a brief introduction to the topic of the lesson, followed by instructional text that presents essential information in short, easy-to-understand sections. Each section of instructional text is followed by a practice activity that lets students apply what they have just learned. A unit review is provided at the end of each unit to assess students' progress. The review is followed by application activities that encourage students to extend and apply what they have learned.

The student text also includes several special features. "Think About It" sections ask students to use critical-thinking skills. "Tip" sections give students useful hints to help them remember specific pieces of information in the student text. "In Real Life" sections show students how the material they are learning connects to their own lives, answering the perennial question, "When am I ever going to use this?"

The reference section at the back of the student text includes a summary of rules and other important information presented in the text, a glossary (with pronunciation guide) that includes all vocabulary in the Words to Know sections, and an index to help students locate information in the text.

Record-Keeping Forms

To make record-keeping easier, we have provided a reproducible class chart that you can use to track students' progress. Fill in your students' names, and make copies of the chart for each unit in the student text. Add lesson numbers, lesson titles, and practice numbers as needed. We have also provided a generic grading rubric for the application activities in the student text so that these activities may be assigned for credit, if you wish. You may customize the rubric by adding more grading criteria or adapting the criteria on the sheet to fit your needs.

We're pleased that you have chosen to Power Up your Basic Skills Curriculum with *Power Basics®*!

To the Teacher, *continued*

Guide to Icons

Teacher's Guide

Teaching Tip

Practical suggestions help you to engage students in the learning process.

Differentiation

Different approaches to the content gives all learners the opportunity to connect to the material.

Calculate It

Useful tips and tricks help students get the most from their calculators.

Student Text

Tip

Tips give helpful hints to boost understanding and retention.

Think About It

These sections develop critical-thinking.

In Real Life

These features connect learning concepts to students' lives, answering the perennial question, "When am I ever going to use this?"

Workbook

Reinforcement

Reinforcement activities give students additional opportunities to practice what they have learned.

Multiple Intelligences

Different approaches capitalize on different learning styles and interests to help all students connect to the material.

Extension

Deepen and broaden learning with critical-thinking activities, real-life applications, and more.

Classroom Management

Student Name	Lesson No.: _____ Title: _____								
	Practice #___	Practice #___	Practice #___	Practice #___	Practice #___	Practice #___	Practice #___	Practice #___	Unit Review Score
1.									
2.									
3.									
4.									
5.									
6.									
7.									
8.									
9.									
10.									
11.									
12.									
13.									
14.									
15.									
16.									
17.									
18.									
19.									
20.									
21.									
22.									
23.									
24.									
25.									
26.									
27.									
28.									
29.									
30.									

Application Activity Rubric

Name _____ Date _____

Unit _____ Activity _____

POINTS	4 all of the time	3 most of the time	2 some of the time	1 almost none of the time
followed directions				
organized material well				
used appropriate resources				
completed the entire activity				
showed an understanding of the content				
produced error-free materials				
drew logical conclusions				
where appropriate, listed sources used				

Use Chart

POWER BASICS WORKBOOK	STUDENT TEXT PRACTICE
Unit 1: Building Blocks of Living Things	
Activity 1: Sci-Fi Organism	Practice 1: It's Alive!
Activity 2: Basic Chemistry—Atoms	Practice 2: Basic Chemistry
Activity 3: The Molecules of Life	Practice 3: The Molecules of Life
Activity 4: Cell Structure and Function	Practice 5: Inside a Cell
Activity 5: A Cell Factory	Practice 5: Inside a Cell
Activity 6: Cellular Scientists	Practice 5: Inside a Cell
Activity 7: Differences Between Plant and Animal Cells	Practice 6: Making and Using Energy
Activity 8: Plant Cell Model	Practice 6: Making and Using Energy
Activity 9: Photosynthesis	Practice 6: Making and Using Energy
Activity 10: DNA and RNA Structure	Practice 7: Structure of DNA and RNA
Activity 11: Life on the Edge: The Virus	Practice 7: Structure of DNA and RNA
Activity 12: Cell Reproduction	Practice 11: Meiosis
Activity 13: DNA and Mutations	Practice 12: Mutations
Activity 14: Gene Crossword	Practice 13: Mendel's Experiments
Activity 15: Flipping for Traits	Practice 13: Mendel's Experiments
Activity 16: Punnett Squares	Practice 14: Punnett Squares
Activity 17: Queen Victoria and the Royal Disease	Practice 15: Sex-Linked Traits
Activity 18: Special Adaptations	Practice 17: Adaptation and Variation
Activity 19: Stripes and Spots	Practice 18: Natural Selection
Activity 20: The Life of Charles Darwin	Practice 18: Natural Selection
Activity 21: Domains	Practice 20: Classification
Activity 22: Organizing Life	Practice 20: Classification
Unit 2: Simple Organisms	
Activity 23: Monera—Archaebacteria and Eubacteria	Practice 22: Eubacteria
Activity 24: The Bacteria Around Us	Practice 22: Eubacteria
Activity 25: Drawing Protists	Practice 26: Funguslike Protists
Activity 26: Observing Protists	Practice 26: Funguslike Protists
Activity 27: Protists and Humans	Practice 26: Funguslike Protists
Activity 28: Mushroom Lab	Practice 27: What Are Fungi?
Activity 29: Mushroom Model	Practice 27: What Are Fungi?
Activity 30: Fungus Flowchart	Practice 27: What Are Fungi?
Activity 31: Useful Fungi	Practice 27: What Are Fungi?
Unit 3: The Plant Kingdom	
Activity 32: Plant Cells	Practice 28: Plant Cells
Activity 33: Light and Plants	Practice 29: Photosynthesis
Activity 34: Leaves and Roots in the Desert	Practice 32: Stems
Activity 35: Roots Underwater	Practice 31: Roots

Use Chart, *continued*

POWER BASICS WORKBOOK	STUDENT TEXT PRACTICE
Activity 36: What Stops the Tallest Stems?	Practice 32: Stems
Activity 37: Tropism	Practice 33: Tropism
Activity 38: Simple Plants	Practice 35: Vascular Plants
Activity 39: Fruit or Vegetable?	Practice 36: Seed Plants
Activity 40: Plant Flowchart	Practice 36: Seed Plants
Activity 41: Where Does Paper Come From?	Practice 36: Seed Plants
Activity 42: Making Paper	Practice 36: Seed Plants
Activity 43: Herbal Medicine	Practice 36: Seed Plants

Unit 4: The Animal Kingdom

Activity 44: Marine Invertebrates	Practice 40: Arthropods
Activity 45: Go With the Flowchart	Practice 40: Arthropods
Activity 46: Model a Marine Invertebrate	Practice 40: Arthropods
Activity 47: Marine Invertebrate Classification	Practice 40: Arthropods
Activity 48: Marine Invertebrate Research	Practice 40: Arthropods
Activity 49: Terrestrial and Freshwater Invertebrates	Practice 40: Arthropods
Activity 50: Ecosystems of Terrestrial and Freshwater Invertebrates	Practice 40: Arthropods
Activity 51: Arthropods	Practice 40: Arthropods
Activity 52: Arthropod Classification	Practice 40: Arthropods
Activity 53: Fishy Characteristics	Practice 41: Chordates and the First Vertebrates
Activity 54: Fish Models	Practice 41: Chordates and the First Vertebrates
Activity 55: How Do Fish Breathe?	Practice 41: Chordates and the First Vertebrates
Activity 56: Amphibian Characteristics	Practice 42: Amphibians
Activity 57: Characteristics of Non-Amniotic Vertebrates	Practice 42: Amphibians
Activity 58: Reptile Poster	Practice 43: Reptiles
Activity 59: Break an Egg	Practice 44: Birds
Activity 60: Amniotic Egg	Practice 44: Birds
Activity 61: Birds of a Feather	Practice 44: Birds
Activity 62: Compare and Contrast	Practice 44: Birds
Activity 63: Mammal Crossword	Practice 45: Mammals
Activity 64: Mammal Essay	Practice 45: Mammals
Activity 65: Group Characteristics	Practice 45: Mammals

Unit 5: The Human Body

Activity 66: Over the Lips, Through the Gums, Look Out, Stomach, Here It Comes	Practice 46: The Digestive Tract
Activity 67: Digestive System Table	Practice 46: The Digestive Tract
Activity 68: Processing the Food Groups	Practice 47: Absorption of Nutrients
Activity 69: Excretion Word Search	Practice 48: Processing Wastes

Use Chart, *continued*

POWER BASICS WORKBOOK	STUDENT TEXT PRACTICE
Activity 70: No Smoking!	Practice 49: The Respiratory System
Activity 71: Respiration and Circulation Matchup	Practice 50: The Circulatory System
Activity 72: Heart and Lung	Practice 50: The Circulatory System
Activity 73: Heart to Heart	Practice 50: The Circulatory System
Activity 74: Viruses	Practice 51: Pathogens
Activity 75: White Blood Cell Superhero!	Practice 52: Physical and Chemical Defenses
Activity 76: Mothers and Smallpox	Practice 53: The Immune System
Activity 77: Stopping the Sweat	Practice 54: Skin
Activity 78: Skeletal and Muscular Systems	Practice 56: Muscles
Activity 79: Muscle Elasticity	Practice 56: Muscles
Activity 80: The Neuron	Practice 57: Neurons
Activity 81: Quick Reflexes	Practice 57: Neurons
Activity 82: Sense-abilities	Practice 58: The Senses
Activity 83: The Brain	Practice 59: The Central Nervous System
Activity 84: Hormones	Practice 60: The Endocrine System
Activity 85: Reproductive System	Practice 62: Female Reproductive System
Activity 86: Reproductive Systems Matchup	Practice 62: Female Reproductive System
Activity 87: Fetal Development	Practice 62: Female Reproductive System
Activity 88: Developmental Psychology	Practice 62: Female Reproductive System
Activity 89: Systems of the Body	Practice 62: Female Reproductive System

Unit 6: Ecology

POWER BASICS WORKBOOK	STUDENT TEXT PRACTICE
Activity 90: Being an Ecologist	Practice 66: Changes in Ecosystems
Activity 91: The Food Chain	Practice 64: The Energy Cycle
Activity 92: Crop Rotation	Practice 66: Changes in Ecosystems
Activity 93: Losing the Frogs	Practice 66: Changes in Ecosystems
Activity 94: Carnivorous Plants	Practice 66: Changes in Ecosystems
Activity 95: Interactions	Practice 70: Symbiosis
Activity 96: Symbiosis	Practice 70: Symbiosis
Activity 97: Temperate and Tropical Rain Forests	Practice 71: Tropical Rain Forests
Activity 98: Charting the Rain Forest	Practice 71: Tropical Rain Forests
Activity 99: Biomes	Practice 75: Tundra

Unit 1: Building Blocks of Living Things

Unit 1 presents the concepts students will need as a foundation for studying biology. Lesson 1 discusses the organic molecules that form the basis of life. Lesson 2 addresses the structure of living things, cells, and how cells make and use energy. The third lesson introduces the concepts of DNA and RNA and how proteins are synthesized. The fourth lesson presents the life cycle of the cell, including mitosis, meiosis, and cell mutations. Lesson 5 introduces genetics and heredity, including Mendel's early experiments and recent advances in genetics. Lesson 6 addresses evolution, including adaptation, variation, and natural selection. The last lesson in this unit discusses classification and taxonomy, with an overview of the six-kingdom model.

Lesson 1—Characteristics of Living Things

Goal: To learn about the basic organic molecules that form the basis of life

WORDS TO KNOW

amino acids	enzymes	organic molecules
atoms	glucose	organism
carbohydrates	lipids	reproduction
element	molecules	solvent
energy	offspring	spontaneous generation

Lesson 2—Cells

Goal: To learn about the structure of cells and the biological processes that go on inside cells

WORDS TO KNOW

active transport	cytoplasm	lysosomes
ATP (adenosine triphosphate)	dark phase	membrane
cell wall	diffusion	mitochondria
cells	endoplasmic reticulum (ER)	nuclear envelope
cellulose	Golgi complex	nucleoli (sing. *nucleolus*)
chlorophyll	impermeable	nucleus
chloroplasts	light phase	organelles

osmosis	photosynthesis	transport
passive transport	respiration	vacuoles
permeable	ribosomes	
phosphate	semipermeable	

Lesson 3—Nucleotides and Protein Synthesis

Goal: To understand the structure of DNA and RNA; to understand how these molecules direct the construction of proteins

WORDS TO KNOW

adenine	guanine	RNA polymerase
anticodons	messenger RNA (mRNA)	start codon
chromosomes	nitrogen-containing base	stop codon
codons	nucleic acids	thymine
cytosine	nucleotides	transcription
deoxyribonucleic acid (DNA)	ribonucleic acid (RNA)	transfer RNA (tRNA)
deoxyribose	ribose	translation
double helix	ribosomal RNA (rRNA)	uracil

Lesson 4—The Cell Cycle

Goal: To understand how cells replicate; to understand how new copies of chromosomes are made

WORDS TO KNOW

anaphase	diploid cells	histones
autosome	DNA polymerase	homologous
centriole	egg	interphase
chromatid	fertilization	M phase
chromatin	gametes	meiosis
crossing over	gene	meiotic interphase
daughter cells	haploid cells	metaphase

mitosis	sex cells	telophase
mutagens	sister chromatids	translocation
mutation	sperm	tumor
nondisjunction	spindle	
prophase	substitution	

Lesson 5—Genetics and Heredity

Goal: To understand how traits get passed from generation to generation

WORDS TO KNOW

allele	heterozygous	Punnett square
codominance	homozygous	recessive
dominant	phenotype	sex-linked
genotype	polygenic traits	zygote

Lesson 6—Evolution

Goal: To learn about the forces that drive evolution

WORDS TO KNOW

adaptation	gene pool	sexual reproduction
behavioral adaptation	natural selection	speciation
evolution	physical adaptation	species
fitness	populations	variation
fossil record	resource partitioning	

Lesson 7—Organizing Life

Goal: To understand how organisms are classified

WORDS TO KNOW

ancestor	division	mnemonic
classes	families	orders
classification	genera (plural of *genus*)	phylum (plural *phyla*)
classify	kingdoms	taxonomy

Notes on Application Activities in Student Text

Activity	Skills Applied	Product
Diffusion Through a Selective Membrane	observing, collecting data, analyzing data, making conclusions	model
Comparing Plant and Animal Cells	observing, using a microscope, diagramming, labeling	diagrams
Genetic Probability Is Like Flipping a Coin	making predictions, collecting data, analyzing data	model
A Model of Meiosis	following directions, making a model, drawing conclusions	model

Additional Activity Suggestions

■ To explain triplet codons, try writing four letters on the board—A,E,R, and T, work well. Have students write as many meaningful three-letter words as they can using any combination of three letters from the list (i.e., are, art, ate, ear, eat, rat, tar, tea). This activity will demonstrate how meaningful "triplets" can be spelled from four bases in DNA.

■ Ask students to try to make a model of meiosis for an organism with a total of six chromosomes. Stress that no matter how many total chromosomes an organism has, the meiotic process is the same and gametes, eggs, and sperm with half the total number of chromosomes are produced. In this way, offspring inherit half of their chromosomes from each parent.

■ Have students go to the library and research the discovery of the DNA molecule. Ask them to trace the steps James Watson and Francis Crick took to discover the structure of the molecule (and win the Nobel Prize for their efforts).

Teaching Tips

- Ask your students to visualize the length of DNA. If the DNA in a single human cell were stretched out and laid end to end, it would measure almost 2 meters. The average human body contains 10 to 20 billion miles of DNA distributed among trillions of cells.

- Honeycombs are made of wax, a kind of lipid. Ask your students the following question: What might happen if a honeycomb were made of a carbohydrate such as sucrose? Answer: Honey would dissolve the comb.

Differentiation

- Have students attempt to replicate the results of the spontaneous generation hypothesis by this simple experiment. Boil two flasks of chicken broth until both are sterile. Immediately seal one of them by covering the top with plastic wrap tightly. Leave the other open to the air. Within days, your students will note that the unsealed broth has become cloudy. Carefully take a sample from each flask, and make vital slides. Look at both samples under a microscope. What do the students notice? Elicit questions about why there is a difference. Where did the microbes in the free-air sample come from?

- Have students make a 3-D model of the animal cell and describe how each organelle performs its functions.

- Ask students to make a side-by-side comparison of meiosis and mitosis using diagrams.

- Over time, students can actually replicate Mendel's pea experiments. Peas have several life cycles over each growing season. Have the students record their observations using Punnett Squares.

- In your classroom, use fossil imprints (make by using latex molds filled with plaster of paris) and create a poster or wall showing how life forms appear in the fossil record.

- Assign a specific organism to individual students or to student groups. Have them create a taxonomic chart that shows kingdom, phylum (or division), class, order, family, genus, and species for their organism.

Unit 2: Simple Organisms

Unit 2 introduces Earth's simplest organisms: bacteria, protists, and fungi. Lesson 8 gives an overview of archaebacteria and eubacteria, with a brief introduction to viruses. Lesson 9 discusses the protist kingdom, including plantlike protists, animallike protists, and funguslike protists. Lesson 10 presents the role, structure, and diversity of fungi.

Lesson 8—Archaebacteria and Eubacteria

Goal: To learn about archaebacteria and eubacteria

WORDS TO KNOW

anaerobic

antibiotics

archaebacteria

bacilli (singular *bacillus*)

bacteria (singular *bacterium*)

binary fission

cocci (singular *coccus*)

eubacteria

flagella

gram-negative

gram-positive

microscopic

nucleoid

prokaryote

spirilla (singular *spirillum*)

viruses

Lesson 9—Protists

Goal: To learn about the different classes of protists

WORDS TO KNOW

algae (singular *alga*)

algal bloom

cilia

eukaryote

parasites

plasmodium

protist

protozoans

pseudopod

spores

toxin

Lesson 10—Fungi

Goal: To learn about the structure, function, and diversity of fungi

WORDS TO KNOW

filament	hypha (plural *hyphae*)	symbiotic
fungi (singular *fungus*)	lichen	
germinate	mycelium	

Notes on Application Activities in Student Text

Activity	Skills Applied	Products
Yeast Population Analysis	interpreting data, graphing, analyzing information	chart, graph
Bacteria Shapes	collecting samples, following a procedure, making inferences, analysis	labeled sketches
Grow a Bread Mold	observing, following a procedure	sketches

Additional Activity Suggestions

■ Ask students to research the three kinds of protists and distinguish between them by their lifestyle (animallike, plantlike, and funguslike). Make a chart showing how the organisms fall into one or the other category. Ask them to explain how a given organism has animallike, plantlike, or funguslike tendencies.

■ Have students consider the differences between archaebacteria and eubacteria. In which environments would they be likely to encounter archaebacteria? Eubacteria? Can archaebacteria cause disease in humans? Why or why not?

■ Go on a fungus hunt. Collect mushrooms, toadstools, truffles, morels, and lichens. Make sure that you remind students that such fungi can be poisonous, and that they should be very careful to wash their hands after handling any fungus. Get a local field guide and have students identify and label each fungus. Spray all fungi with hairspray to preserve them for display.

Calculate It

- Bacteria reproduce exponentially. If there are 10 cells, after a given time, there will be 20 cells, then 40, then 80, then 160. The function that models this growth curve is 10×2^t, where t is the number of divisions that take place in a given time. If bacteria reproduce 4 times per hour, $t = 4$. Have your students use a calculator to calculate data points, then plot a graph to show the exponential curve.

Differentiation

- Collect water samples from a local pond. In the classroom, ask students to use a microscope and field guides to identify protists and bacteria.

- Create a poster showing the internal differences between a prokaryote cell (such as an archaebacterium or eubacterium) and a eukaryote cell (such as a protist).

- Have students collect samples of each of the three "lifestyles" of protists—animallike, plantlike, and funguslike. Have them identify their samples. *Note:* All animallike protists will be microscopic.

- Ask students to choose one fungus and write a first-person narrative telling its life story.

Unit 3: The Plant Kingdom

In Unit 3, students learn about the plant kingdom. Lesson 11 covers basic plant anatomy and the process of photosynthesis, which is common to all plants, as well as other functions of plants. Lesson 12 discusses the simple, spore-bearing plants, such as mosses, worts, and ferns and the difference between nonvascular and vascular plants. It also addresses the life cycles of plants, the difference between conifers and flowering plants, and the differences between monocots and dicots.

Lesson 11—Plant Biology

Goal: To learn about the structure and function of plants

WORDS TO KNOW

bud	hydrotropism	stem
cambium	leaves	stomata (singular *stoma*)
cellulose	legumes	taproots
fibrous root system	phloem	transpiration
gravitropism	phototropism	tropism
hormones	roots	xylem

Lesson 12—Plant Diversity

Goal: To learn about the major groups of plants in the world today

WORDS TO KNOW

anthers	lycopod	prothallus
conifers	monocot	rhizomes
dicot	nectar	sepals
embryo	nonvascular plants	stigma
ferns	ovary	style
filaments	petals	succulent
fronds	pistil	vascular plants
gymnosperms	pollen	
horsetails	pollination	

Notes on Application Activities in Student Text

Activity	Skills Applied	Product
Photosynthesis	observing, collecting data, graphing, analyzing data, drawing conclusions	graph
Plant Overcrowding	observing, taking measurements, graphing, interpreting data	graph

Additional Activity Suggestions

- Bring in a section of a log from a freshly cut tree. Have students determine how old the tree is by counting the rings. The distance between rings tells how much the tree grew that year. Growth is based on the availability of water, nutrients, and weather conditions. Show students which years seemed to be better seasons than others.

- Ask students to make leaf collections. Have them choose leaves that represent a variety of shapes and sizes—single leaves, compound leaves, leaves with parallel venation, leaves with netted venation. Have students identify the plants the leaves came from using leaf identification books.

 ## Teaching Tip

- Reinforce to students that the complexity of an organism does not depend on the amount of DNA in its cells. A species of fern (*Ophioglossum reticulatum*) has the largest number of chromosomes—1260 (630 pairs).

 ## Differentiation

- Collect plants (or parts of plants) of all types—nonvascular, vascular spore-bearing, cone-bearing, and seed-bearing. Have students organize them by division, then show their taxonomic groupings.

- Outdoors in a park, field, or wooded area, mark off 1 meter square areas with string and stakes. In small groups, have students observe and identify each plant in their area using local field guides. Ask them to notice the difference in height, light requirements, water requirements, and nutrient requirements for each plant. How can the plants live together in such close quarters?

- Have students use the Internet to research toxic plants. Where is the toxic agent located—leaves, stem, fruit, flower, root, seed? Which chemicals make plants toxic or unpalatable? Within each plant's biome, how does the toxicity help the plant or its seeds survive? Have students create a "wanted" poster that includes a drawing or photograph of the plant they researched, information about its deadly nature, and where the plant can be found in the wild.

Unit 4: The Animal Kingdom

This unit addresses animal life except for human life, which is discussed in the following unit. Lesson 13 introduces invertebrates such as sponges, worms, and mollusks. Lesson 14 covers vertebrate animals, starting with fish, the earliest vertebrates, then moves on to amphibians, reptiles, birds, and mammals.

Lesson 13—Invertebrates

Goal: To survey the major groups of animals that lack backbones

WORDS TO KNOW

abdomen	crustaceans	platyhelminthes
amoebocytes	exoskeleton	polyp
annelids	gastropods	pores
antennae	gills	poriferan
arachnids	hemocoels	pseudocoelom
arthropods	insects	secrete
bivalves	invertebrate	shell
carapace	larvae (singular *larva*)	sponges
cephalopods	mantle	tentacles
cephalothorax	medusa	thorax
chelicerae	mesoglea	trachea
chelicerates	mollusks	unirames
chitin	molting	valves
choanocytes	mucus	visceral mass
closed circulatory system	muscular foot	worm
cnidarian	nematodes	
coeloms	pedipalps	

Lesson 14—Vertebrates

Goal: To learn about chordates and their most important class, the vertebrates

WORDS TO KNOW

amphibian	jawless fish	reptile
bony fish	mammal	sense organs
cartilage	mammary glands	skeleton
cartilaginous fish	marsupial	spinal cord
chordates	metamorphosis	swim bladder
coldblooded	nervous system	vertebrae (singular *vertebra*)
fetus	notochord	vertebrates
gill slits	placental	warmblooded

Notes on Application Activities in Student Text

Activity	Skills Applied	Products
Earthworms and Plant Growth	observing, evaluating ideas, making inferences	models
Comparing Vertebrates	observing, making inferences, analyzing, drawing conclusions	chart, written conclusion
Comparing Variations in Humans	measuring, observing, summarizing, making inferences, drawing conclusions	chart, bar graphs

Additional Activity Suggestions

■ Invite a local veterinarian to speak to students about treating animals for parasitic worms. Have students prepare questions ahead of time. Topics of interest may be how to protect one's animals and oneself from worm infestation. Also, ask the veterinarian to explain the life cycle of one worm and the time of year various worms are most prevalent.

■ Reptiles are easy-to-manage classroom animals. Bring a snake to the classroom and allow students to watch its activities. Feed the snake an egg. Allow students to observe the process of constriction, the unhinging of the jaws, and the swallowing process. Then discuss the process of reptilian digestion.

Differentiation

- Have students research the number of phyla of invertebrates and make a chart of animal phyla. Only one phylum—Chordata—contains vertebrate animals. There are 35 phyla, but only nine of them—Porifera, Cnidaria, Mollusca, Echinodermata, Platyhelminthes, Nemotoda, Annelida, Arthropoda, and Chordata—contain more than one organism. Have students make a chart of the nine common phyla and name common animals in each phylum.

- Have students research and make models of a single small ecosystem (for instance, the understory of a temperate rain forest) within any biome. The model should be split in half. The first half should show the daytime life of the biome; the second half should show the nighttime life of the biome. Have students label each organism and describe its activity. Remind students to include all animal life—vertebrate and invertebrate.

- Try to keep different organisms in your classroom, vertebrates and invertebrates, for student observation. Animals in captivity behave differently from the same animals in the wild, so you should also have your class study living organisms in the field as often as possible.

Unit 5: The Human Body

This unit introduces human anatomy and physiology. Lesson 15 covers the digestive system, from ingesting food to processing it and excreting waste. Lesson 16 moves on to the respiratory and circulatory systems, explaining their components, structure, and function. In Lesson 17, students learn about some of the pathogens that attack the human body and how the body defends itself against these pathogens. Lessons 18, 19, and 20 present the structure and functions of the skin, skeleton, and muscle systems of the body. Lesson 21 introduces the central and peripheral nervous systems, the endocrine system, and the senses of touch, smell, taste, hearing, and sight. Lesson 22 addresses human reproduction, from the male and female reproductive systems to fertilization and pregnancy.

Lesson 15—Digestion and Excretion

Goal: To learn about the organs and glands of the digestive system; to learn about the function of the kidneys

WORDS TO KNOW

antioxidants	esophagus	liver
anus	essential amino acids	loop of Henle
appendix	fat-soluble	maltose
bile	feces	medulla
bladder	food pyramid	nephrons
Bowman's capsule	gallbladder	pancreas
capillaries	glomerulus	pepsin
cecum	glucagon	peristalsis
chyme	glycogen	pharynx
coenzymes	hydrochloric acid	rectum
collecting duct	ileum	renal artery
colon	insulin	renal pelvis
cortex	jejunum	renal vein
digestive tract	kidneys	saliva
duodenum	large intestine	salivary glands
epiglottis	lipase	serum proteins

stomach	urea	villi (sing. *villus*)
taste buds	ureter	water-soluble
tongue	urethra	

Lesson 16—Respiration and Circulation

Goal: To learn about the lungs and gas exchange; to learn about the components of the circulatory and lymphatic systems

WORDS TO KNOW

alveoli	diastolic pressure	pulmonary veins
aorta	heart	red blood cells
arteries	hemoglobin	systolic pressure
arterioles	larynx	thoracic cavity
atmospheric pressure	lymph	thoracic duct
atrium (plural *atria*)	lymph nodes	trachea
bronchi (singular *bronchus*)	lymphatic system	valves
bronchioles	mucous membrane	veins
carbonic acid	nodes	ventricle
cilia	pacemaker	venules
coronary arteries	partial pressure	vocal cords
diaphragm	pulmonary artery	

Lesson 17—Fighting Invaders

Goal: To learn how your body defends itself against invaders

WORDS TO KNOW

allergies	antiserums	binding sites
antibodies	autoimmune diseases	histamine
antigen	B-cells	immune

immune system	macrophage	platelets
interferons	mutate	prion
keratin	pathogens	T-cells
lymphocytes	phagocytes	white blood cells

Lesson 18—The Skin

Goal: To understand the structure and function of skin

WORDS TO KNOW

collagen	follicle	sebum
dermis	ground substance	skin
elastin	hair	subcutaneous layer
epidermis	mast cells	sweat
fibroblasts	melanin	sweat glands

Lesson 19—Bones

Goal: To understand the function of the human skeleton

WORDS TO KNOW

appendicular skeleton	joints	spongy bone
axial skeleton	ligaments	stem cells
compact bone	marrow	sternum
cranium	osteocytes	synovial fluid
disk	pectoral girdle	synovial membrane
Haversian canal	pelvic girdle	vertebral column
Haversian systems	shaft	

Lesson 20—Muscles

Goal: To understand the muscles in the human body and learn their functions

WORDS TO KNOW

actin	muscles	skeletal muscles
ADP (adenosine diphosphate)	myosin	smooth muscles
cardiac muscle	myosin heads	tendons
fibers	sarcomere	
inhibitors	sarcoplasmic reticula	

Lesson 21—Nervous and Endocrine Systems

Goal: To learn about the two systems that enable different parts of the body to communicate with one another

WORDS TO KNOW

adrenal glands	effectors	meninges
adrenaline	endocrine system	metabolism
autonomic nervous system	epinephrine	motor cortex
axons	frontal lobe	myelin sheath
blood-brain barrier	glands	nervous system
calcium gate	growth hormone	neurons
central nervous system	hemispheres	neurotransmitters
cerebellum	hindbrain	nodes of Ranvier
cerebral cortex	hormones	norepinephrine
cerebrum	hypothalamus	occipital lobe
chemoreceptors	incus	optic nerve
cochlea	insulin	pancreas
cones	ion	parietal lobe
cornea	iris	pituitary gland
cortisol	lens	polarization
dendrites	limbic system	prefrontal area
depolarization	malleus	pupil
ear canal	medulla	resting state

© 2005 Walch Publishing

retina	stimuli	thermoreceptors
rods	synaptic gap	thyroid
Schwann cells	synaptic knobs	thyroid stimulating hormone (TSH)
sclera	synaptic vesicles	
sensory receptors	taste buds	thyroxin
somatic nervous system	temporal lobe	tympanum
stapes	thalamus	vitreous humor

Lesson 22—Reproductive System

Goal: To learn about the anatomy of the male and female reproductive systems, the development of sperm and eggs, and fertilization

WORDS TO KNOW

amniotic sac	luteinizing hormone (LH)	secondary sexual characteristics
blastocyst	menstrual cycle	semen
blastoderm	mesoderm	seminal vesicles
chorion	oogenesis	Sertoli cells
corpus luteum	oogonia	spermatids
ectoderm	ovaries	spermatocytes
ejaculation	oviduct	spermatogenesis
endoderm	ovulation	spermatozoa
endometrium	penis	testes
estrogen	placenta	testosterone
fallopian tube	primary oocytes	trimesters
follicle	progesterone	uterus
follicle stimulating hormone (FSH)	prolactin	vagina
	prostate gland	vas deferens
gastrulation	relaxin	
inhibin	scrotum	

Notes on Application Activities in Student Text

Activity	Skills Applied	Product
Iron It Out	taking measurements, making inferences, drawing conclusions	iron extracted from food
Take a Breather	observing, collecting data, analyzing data	comparison of CO_2 output
Lip Saver	applying concepts, observation, analyzing observations	model
Tensed Up	observing, making inferences, drawing conclusions	demonstration of muscle tension
Interactive Hormones	showing relationships, making inferences, drawing conclusions, evaluating data	chart

Additional Activity Suggestions

■ Have a representative of the American Heart and Lung Association visit to speak about the ways to prevent heart and lung disease. Have students write questions on note cards to ask the speaker. Topics might include the effects of smoking, of a high-fat diet, of second-hand smoke, or of a high-fiber diet.

■ Invite a health care worker who specializes in diabetes to speak to the class. Ask the person to explain how diabetes tests are done and how diabetes is treated. Also ask the person to explain what can happen if diabetes goes untreated.

■ Demonstrate how the diaphragm affects air pressure in the body. Place a one-hole stopper in the neck of a bell jar. Use petroleum jelly as a seal. Attach two small balloons securely to the ends of a Y-shaped tube. Insert this tube into the stopper so the two branches of the Y are in the jar. Attach a thin rubber membrane over the lower surface of the bell jar. This will decrease the air pressure around the balloons in the bell jar. Pull the membrane down gently. This decreases the pressure around the balloons in the bell jar. Air should flow into the balloons to make the pressure inside and outside the jar equal. Lead students in a discussion of how this result illustrates what happens to the lungs when the diaphragm contracts. Press the membrane upward. This will cause the balloons to deflate, illustrating exhalation.

 ## Teaching Tips

■ Have students calculate the volume of air that passes through the lungs in a certain time period. A person usually takes in about 500 ml of air with each breath. Have students count the number of times they breathe in one minute while sitting quietly. Using that number, have them calculate the volume of air they inhale and exhale in one hour, day, week, and year.

- Ask three students to wear earplugs and three others to wear blindfolds for the first 20 minutes of lesson time. Conduct the lesson as you normally would. Then encourage the six people to describe their experiences. Have the six compare their experiences to what actually went on. Discuss how challenges to one's sensory system can affect a person's understanding, ability to learn, and ability to function in society.

- Students often think that lack of oxygen causes one to breathe harder and one's heart rate to increase. Be sure they understand that it is not a lack of oxygen, but rather an increase of carbon dioxide that triggers the brain to increase breathing and heart rate so the body can get rid of this poisonous waste product.

 ## Differentiation

- Under close supervision, ask students to choose some typical food items and place them in a large flask with about 50 mL of hydrochloric acid. Gently swirl the items to simulate the churning action of the stomach. As the students watch, the food particles begin to dissolve. Now, with the flask on a bench or table, have the students add antacid tablets, such as TUMS®. Ask them to describe and explain what happens.

- Ask students to research risk factors for skin cancer and develop a prevention program for a local elementary or middle school. The most important risk factor is direct exposure to the sun; sunscreens offer some protection but do not completely prevent exposure. Most exposure to the sun occurs in people younger than 18.

- Get a copy of the 1966 film *Fantastic Voyage* or the book by Isaac Asimov, and either show the film or read parts of the book to your class. Remind the students that the story is science fiction, and ask them which parts of the story are scientifically correct and which are strictly fantasy.

Unit 6: Ecology

In the last unit of this book, students will learn how all the living things they have studied interact with one another. Lesson 23 introduces the concept of ecosystems and ecology. It presents the energy cycle, nutrient cycles, and changes in ecosystems, both natural and human-caused. Lesson 24 moves on to the way organisms within an ecosystem interact, both through competition and through predation. It discusses protective adaptations such as camouflage, chemical defenses, and mimicry. It also presents ways that organisms can live in symbiosis with one another, including parasitism, commensalism, and mutualism. Lesson 25 introduces the six major biomes of Earth—tropical rain forests, deserts, grasslands, deciduous forests and taiga, and tundra—with information about distribution, plants, and animals of each biome.

Lesson 23—Ecosystems

Goal: To learn about the field of ecology; to understand the processes that go on inside ecosystems

WORDS TO KNOW

carbon dioxide	extinct	precipitation
carnivore	food chain	primary consumers
community	food pyramid	producers
decomposers	food web	secondary consumers
ecologist	greenhouse effect	succession
ecology	habitat	tertiary consumers
ecosystem	herbivore	
evaporation	omnivore	

Lesson 24—Interactions

Goal: To understand the ways in which organisms interact with one another;
to understand how these interactions shape evolution

WORDS TO KNOW

camouflage	intraspecific competition	predation
commensalism	mimicry	predator
competition	mutualism	prey
herbivory	niche	specialize
interspecific competition	parasitism	symbiosis

Lesson 25—Biomes

Goal: To understand the six major types of biomes in the world

WORDS TO KNOW

biome	epiphytes	taiga
deciduous forests	grassland	tropical rain forests
desert	permafrost	tundra

Notes on Application Activities in Student Text

Activity	Skills Applied	Product
Decaying Log Community	observing, collecting, analyzing data, drawing conclusions	profile of a community
Water Community Succession	observing, collecting data, evaluating information, drawing conclusions, making inferences	model of an ecosystem

Additional Activity Suggestions

■ Give students a list of organisms (plant and animal) that live in your community. Have them design a food web that shows the interrelationships among these organisms. Have them illustrate the food web on a poster or in a diorama.

Teaching Tips

■ Students' interest is often increased when they work on the Internet. Use the Internet to get students to discuss environmental conservation. Begin by talking about how plants are important to the environment. Focus on what they have learned in Animal and Plant Cell Biology. Then have students explore an Internet site, such as those of the National Arbor Day Foundation or the Nature Conservancy, to see what efforts are being made to preserve the natural environment today. Or, do the same exercise with animals, and discuss the endangered status of certain species and how they became endangered. Good sites for this project include World Wildlife Fund and International Wildlife Education and Conservation.

■ Get students involved in a real ecosystem. Arrange a walking tour of a forest, bog, or lake area. Have a guide help students note the physical boundaries of the ecosystem. Point out populations inhabiting the area. Have students define the habitat of each population and what components make up its niche.

Differentiation

■ Using diagrams, encourage students to show the relationships between animal life and plant life. Remind students that animals are dependent upon plants for more than food. In many important ways, plants are dependent upon animals, as well. Students should remember natural cycles, including the water cycle, the nitrogen cycle, and the carbon cycle.

■ Have students create "A Year in the Life of . . ." models in the medium of their choice. Each student should select a biome, and show how the living and nonliving things in the biome change as the year progresses.

■ Choose a biome. Have students research to find out about all the living things in that biome and the relationships among species in the biome. Is a species a predator or prey? Is a species a producer, a consumer, or a decomposer? Which species are scavengers? Which are producers? What types of symbiotic relationships have been formed among these species? Have students create a table that outlines the role of an organism, its position in the food chain, and its symbiotic relationships with other organisms.

■ Obtain skulls of various animals from the same biome (your local science or natural history museum often has traveling kits of skulls and other natural artifacts that you can borrow). Do not tell the students which animals the skulls came from. Have them observe the teeth of each skull, if any, and make some determinations about the animal's diet, position in the food chain, and age.

Answer Key

Unit 1: Building Blocks of Living Things

Lesson 1: Characteristics of Living Things

Think About It, page 6

Answers will vary. Redi needed something to compare the other flasks with. Had Redi not shown that maggots appear on meat in open flasks, critics could have argued that conditions were not right for spontaneous generation. Critics would argue that it was for that reason maggots did not appear on the meat in the closed flasks.

Practice 1: It's Alive!

1. T		3. F	
2. T		4. T	

Practice 2: Basic Chemistry

1. T		4. T	
2. F		5. F	
3. F			

Practice 3: The Molecules of Life

1. F		3. T	
2. F		4. T	

Lesson 2: Cells

Think About It, page 17

Answers will vary. The concentration of dissolved particles in the intravenous fluid must match the concentration of dissolved particles inside the blood cells. If the intravenous fluid solution is too concentrated, water will leave the blood cells, and the blood cells will shrivel up. If the concentration is too diluted, water will flow into the blood cells, and they will swell and burst.

Practice 4: Cell Membranes

1. F		4. T	
2. F		5. T	
3. T			

Think About It, page 20

Answers will vary. If the enzymes escaped from the lysosomes, they would damage the rest of the cell.

Practice 5: Inside a Cell

1. b, d, g		4. e	
2. c		5. h, f	
3. a			

Practice 6: Making and Using Energy

1. c		4. a	
2. b, d		5. e	
3. f			

Lesson 3: Nucleotides and Protein Synthesis

Think About It, page 29

Answers will vary. In DNA, the A's always pair with the T's, and the C's always pair with the G's. Therefore, the number of A's should equal the number of T's, and the number of C's should equal the number of G's.

Practice 7: Structure of DNA and RNA

1. T		3. F	
2. T		4. F	

Practice 8: Protein Synthesis

1. T		5. F	
2. F		6. T	
3. T		7. T	
4. T			

Lesson 4: The Cell Cycle

Practice 9: Chromosomes

1. b		3. a	
2. e, f		4. c, d	

Practice 10: Mitosis

1. d		4. b	
2. a		5. c	
3. e			

Practice 11: Meiosis

1. c		4. e	
2. b		5. d	
3. a			

Think About It, page 52

Answers will vary. Each amino acid is coded for by more than one codon. For example, AAT and AAC both code for leu.

Practice 12: Mutations

1. b		3. a	
2. c			

Lesson 5: Genetics and Heredity

Practice 13: Mendel's Experiments

1. T
2. T
3. F
4. T
5. F

Think About It, page 60

Answers will vary. If the cell were homozygous dominant, all four gametes would have a dominant allele. If the cell were homozygous recessive, all four gametes would have a recessive allele.

Practice 14: Punnett Squares

1. Gg, gg
2. G and g, g and g
3. Gg, Gg, gg, gg
4. 1:1 (half green pod, half yellow pod)

Think About It, page 64

Answers will vary. Yes, but only if the father is color-blind and the mother is heterozygous. In such a case, there is a 50 percent chance that the daughter would be color-blind and a 50 percent chance that a son would be color-blind.

Practice 15: Sex-Linked Traits

1. 0%
2. 50%
3. 50%
4. 100%

Practice 16: Advances in Genetics

1. a
2. c
3. b

Lesson 6: Evolution

Practice 17: Adaptation and Variation

1. e
2. b
3. c
4. a
5. d

Think About It, page 75

Answers will vary. Because there are so few animals, there is less genetic variation. Therefore, there is a smaller chance that some of the dogs have genes that can help them survive the disease.

Practice 18: Natural Selection

1. I
2. D
3. I
4. I
5. D

Practice 19: Evolution in Action

1. T
2. T
3. F
4. T

Lesson 7: Organizing Life

Practice 20: Classification

1. d
2. a
3. b
4. a

Unit 1 Review

1. b
2. d
3. d
4. b
5. c
6. b
7. d
8. a
9. b
10. a

Unit 2: Simple Organisms

Lesson 8: Archaebacteria and Eubacteria

Practice 21: The Oldest Life-Forms

1. c, d or d, c
2. e
3. b
4. a

Practice 22: Eubacteria

1. a
2. c
3. c
4. a

Practice 23: Viruses

1. F
2. T
3. F
4. F
5. T
6. F
7. T

Lesson 9: Protists

Practice 24: Plantlike Protists

1. b
2. a
3. d
4. c

Practice 25: Animallike Protists

1. a
2. c
3. a

Practice 26: Funguslike Protists

1. b
2. a
3. c

Lesson 10: Fungi

Practice 27: What Are Fungi?

1. F
2. F
3. F
4. T
5. T
6. T

Unit 2 Review

1. b	6. c
2. a	7. d
3. c	8. a
4. a	9. b
5. d	10. d

Unit 3: The Plant Kingdom

Lesson 11: Plant Biology

Practice 28: Plant Cells

1. b, c	3. b
2. a, c, d	4. a, b, c

Think About It, page 124

Answers will vary. During photosynthesis, trees remove carbon dioxide from the air and convert it into glucose. They also release oxygen into the air. If you chop down all the trees, less carbon dioxide will be removed and less oxygen will be added.

Practice 29: Photosynthesis

1. F	3. T
2. T	

Practice 30: Leaves

1. d	3. d
2. a	

Practice 31: Roots

1. b, c, d	3. a, b, d
2. a	

Practice 32: Stems

1. F	4. T
2. T	5. F
3. F	6. T

Practice 33: Tropism

1. d	3. b, c
2. a	

Lesson 12: Plant Diversity

Practice 34: Nonvascular Plants

1. b	3. b
2. a	

Practice 35: Vascular Plants

1. a	3. b
2. c	

Think About It, page 142

Answers will vary. The pollen is blown around randomly. The plant needs to produce enough pollen to make sure that some lands on the female part of the plant.

Practice 36: Seed Plants

1. d	4. b
2. f	5. e
3. a	6. c

Unit 3 Review

1. a, f	6. c
2. d	7. a
3. e	8. b
4. c	9. c
5. b	10. b

Unit 4: The Animal Kingdom

Lesson 13: Invertebrates

Practice 37: Poriferan and Cnidarian

1. P	4. C
2. C	5. P
3. C	6. P

Think About It, page 164

Answers will vary. Xylem and phloem transport sugars and water throughout the entire plant. They enable plants to get bigger. Hearts and veins transport nutrients and oxygen throughout the entire animal, enabling the animal to grow bigger and to remain healthy.

Practice 38: The Worms

1. a	3. c
2. b	

Practice 39: Mollusks

1. d	3. b
2. a	4. b

Think About It, page 169

Answers will vary. When an arthropod molts, it loses its protective exoskeleton. It can lose too much water and is vulnerable to attack.

Practice 40: Arthropods

1. c	4. b
2. b	5. b
3. a	

Lesson 14: Vertebrates

Practice 41: Chordates and the First Vertebrates

1. d	3. b
2. d	

Practice 42: Amphibians

1. F   4. F
2. T   5. T
3. F

Practice 43: Reptiles

1. b   3. b
2. c

Think About It, page 183

Answers will vary. You shiver when it is too cold and sweat when it is too hot. Shivering causes you to use muscles and thus your body temperature rises. When you are too hot, you sweat. Sweating causes your body temperature to cool.

Practice 44: Birds

1. a   3. a
2. b

Practice 45: Mammals

1. F   4. F
2. T   5. F
3. T

Unit 4 Review

1. c   6. c
2. a   7. d
3. b   8. c
4. c   9. b
5. c   10. b

Unit 5: The Human Body

Lesson 15: Digestion and Excretion

Think About It, page 196

Answers will vary. An example of a reaction is respiration, which produces carbon dioxide.

Think About It, page 200

Answers will vary. Enzymes capable of breaking down proteins in food can also break down proteins in living cells. Therefore, it is much safer to store these enzymes in their inactive form.

Practice 46: The Digestive Tract

1. b   4. a
2. e   5. c, f, d
3. g

Practice 47: Absorption of Nutrients

1. c   3. b
2. a, d

Practice 48: Processing Wastes

1. b   3. d
2. c   4. e, a

Lesson 16: Respiration and Circulation

Think About It, page 217

Answers will vary. No. The total air pressure inside and outside the container are equal. As the oxygen leaves the container, other gases, such as nitrogen, enter the container. That is because the partial pressure of nitrogen outside the container was greater than the partial pressure of nitrogen inside the container.

Practice 49: The Respiratory System

1. c, b   3. a
2. e   4. d

Practice 50: The Circulatory System

1. c, b, f   4. d
2. g   5. e
3. a

Lesson 17: Fighting Invaders

Practice 51: Pathogens

1. T   4. F
2. T   5. T
3. F

Think About It, page 232

Answers will vary. Sneezing and coughing propel droplets filled with viruses into the air. Other people inhale these droplets and become infected.

Think About It, page 234

Answers will vary. Proteins are heat-sensitive. If your body temperature gets too high, the shape of the enzymes in your body may change. Your body will be less able to carry out essential chemical reactions.

Practice 52: Physical and Chemical Defenses

1. a   3. b
2. c

Practice 53: The Immune System

1. e, c   3. a, c
2. b   4. d

Lesson 18: The Skin

Practice 54: Skin

1. f, e, b   3. a
2. d   4. c

Lesson 19: Bones

Think About It, page 249
Answers will vary. The joint between the two bones in your forearm at your elbow is a pivot joint. It enables you to twist your forearm.

Practice 55: Bones
1. F
2. T
3. F
4. F
5. T

Lesson 20: Muscles

Practice 56: Muscles
1. b
2. e
3. a, d
4. c

Lesson 21: Nervous and Endocrine Systems

Think About It, page 263
Answers will vary. These motor neurons generate their own signals. They do not receive signals from stimuli or other neurons. Therefore, they have no need for dendrites.

Practice 57: Neurons
1. F
2. T
3. T
4. T

Practice 58: The Senses
1. b, e
2. d, g, c
3. a
4. f

Practice 59: The Central Nervous System
1. T
2. F
3. T
4. F

Practice 60: The Endocrine System
1. c
2. b
3. a
4. d

Lesson 22: Reproductive System

Practice 61: Male Reproductive System
1. F
2. F
3. F
4. T

Practice 62: Female Reproductive System
1. T
2. F
3. T
4. T
5. F

Unit 5 Review
1. d
2. d
3. b
4. b
5. b
6. a
7. c
8. T
9. F
10. T

Unit 6: Ecology

Lesson 23: Ecosystems

Practice 63: The Science of Ecology
1. d
2. b
3. c

Think About It, page 307
Answers will vary. Perhaps you live near a farm. The farm has a field where 12 cows are grazing. The field is full of producers: grasses, trees, plants. The 12 cows that eat the producers are primary consumers. The amount of producers outnumber the primary consumers. A family of four lives on the farm and eats the cows. The people are secondary consumers. For this example, the pattern holds true. If you live in a city, there may be a park nearby. The park is full of producers: grasses, trees, and flowers. You will more than likely find many insects and caterpillars in the park. The insects and caterpillars eat the producers and are therefore primary consumers. There may be birds and mice in the park that eat the primary consumers. They are secondary consumers. Perhaps there is a snake that lives in the park that feeds on the rats and birds. The snake is a tertiary consumer. The pattern holds true for this example as well.

Practice 64: The Energy Cycle
1. b
2. a
3. a

Practice 65: Nutrient Cycles
1. W, C, N
2. N
3. C
4. W, C
5. C

Think About It, page 312
Answers will vary. Cherry trees that the tent caterpillar feed on; birds that feed on the cherries; birds and wasps that feed on the tent caterpillars.

Think About It, page 314
Answers will vary. The number of tent caterpillars would increase. The tent caterpillars would reduce the number of cherry trees. Animals that depend on the cherries for food may decrease.

Practice 66: Changes in Ecosystems
1. c
2. a
3. a
4. b

Lesson 24: Interactions

Practice 67: Competition
1. F
2. F
3. T
4. T
5. F

Practice 68: Herbivory
1. b
2. d
3. c

Think About It, page 326
Answers will vary. Predators recognize that the animal is poisonous. Therefore, they won't attack it.

Practice 69: Predation
1. d
2. c
3. d

Practice 70: Symbiosis
1. P
2. M
3. C
4. P
5. M

Lesson 25: Biomes

Think About It, page 331
Answers will vary. Trees drop their leaves in cold weather to conserve water. Tropical rain forests are warm and wet all year long, so trees do not need to conserve as much water.

Practice 71: Tropical Rain Forests
1. T
2. F
3. T
4. F
5. T

Practice 72: Deserts
1. T
2. F
3. T
4. T
5. F

Think About It, page 337
Answers will vary. There is no place to hide on grasslands. Therefore, animals use speed to escape predators. Predators need speed to catch their fast prey.

Practice 73: Grasslands
1. T
2. T
3. F
4. F

Practice 74: Deciduous Forests and Taiga
1. F
2. F
3. T
4. F

Think About It, page 342
Answers will vary. There is less surface area through which heat can be lost.

Practice 75: Tundra
1. T
2. T
3. T
4. F

Unit 6 Review
1. c
2. c
3. b
4. d
5. a
6. d
7. a
8. c
9. a
10. a

Graphic Organizers

Graphic Organizers

Graphic organizers are a versatile teaching and learning tool. They can help students clarify their thinking, integrate new knowledge, reinforce their understanding of a topic, and review material for quizzes and tests. Using graphic organizers, learners can understand content more clearly and can take clear, concise notes. Graphic organizers can also act as a visual aid to make abstract concepts more concrete.

The graphic organizers provided here can be used in many ways. You can use transparencies of the organizers to introduce or review a topic with the entire class. You can photocopy the organizers and allow students to use them as they work through the student text. Here is a brief description of the graphic organizers in this section and their uses.

Web

Information gained from reading can be collected and organized in a web. The web can help students identify categories that fit the information and see relationships among the facts and data. Students can add or subtract information circles and lines as they wish.

Hierarchical Diagram

Defining the relationships between organisms is an important part of biology. The hierarchical diagram is a technique often used to classify these relationships.

Cycle

Things in nature often occur in repeating patterns. A cycle shows the progression of the pattern and how the pattern repeats. Cycle diagrams can be used to show everything from the life cycle of fungi to the way rocks change over time.

Steps in a Process Chart

This graphic organizer is used to show information in order. Students will find this organizer particularly useful when taking notes of mathematical processes, showing the steps in order. They should write the process in the box at the top of the chart, then break the process down into steps and write one step in one box, adding or deleting boxes as needed.

Web

Write the main idea in the center oval. Write the information about the topic in the other ovals. Add or delete lines and ovals as needed.

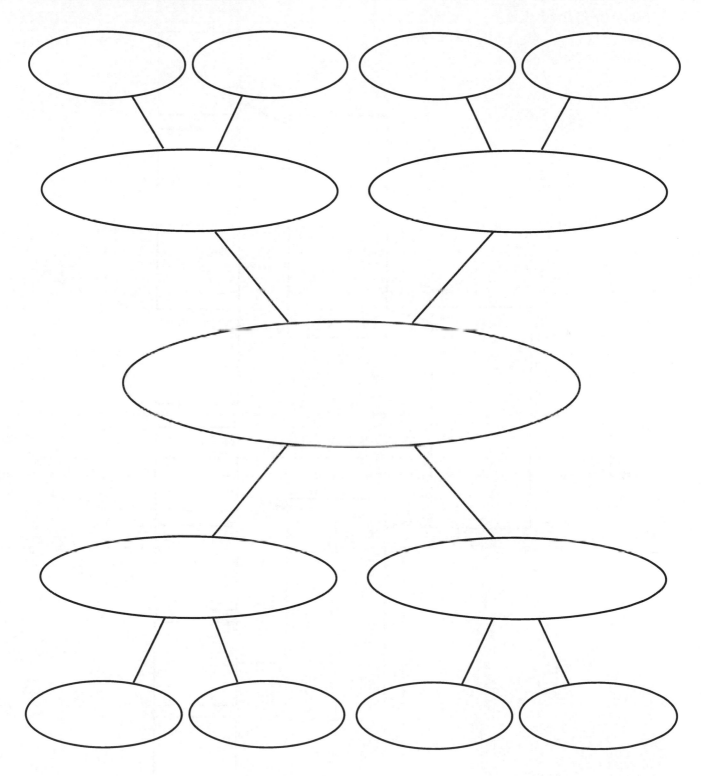

Hierarchical Diagram

Write the root of the hierarchy in the box at the top. Write the next level in the hierarchy in the boxes below the top box. Continue until you have added all the levels in the hierarchy. Add or delete lines and boxes as needed.

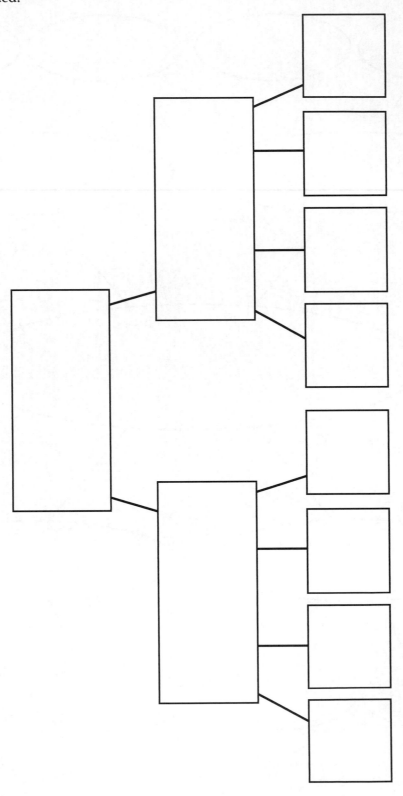

Cycle

Write the important stages of the cycle in the boxes. Add or delete boxes as needed.

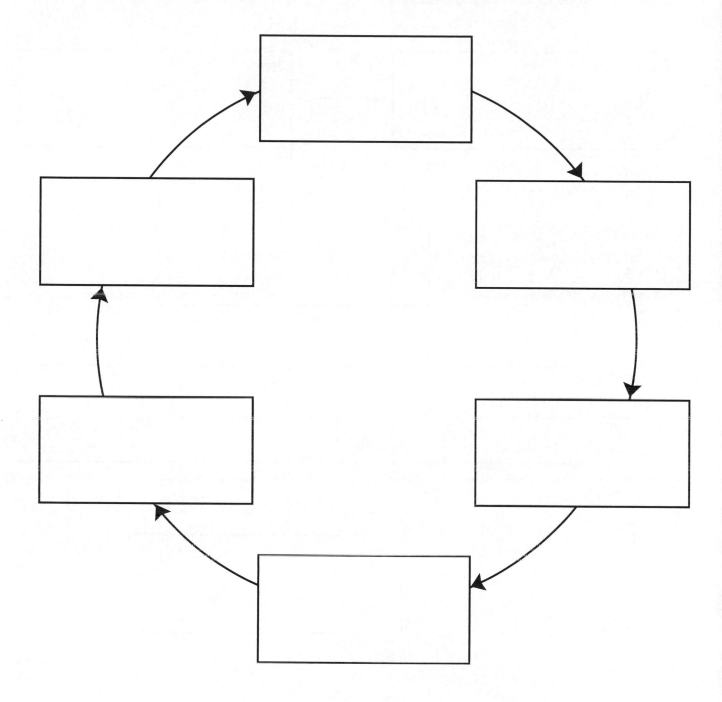

Steps in a Process Chart

Write the first step or event in the first box. Write the other steps or events in order in the other boxes. Add or delete lines and boxes as needed.

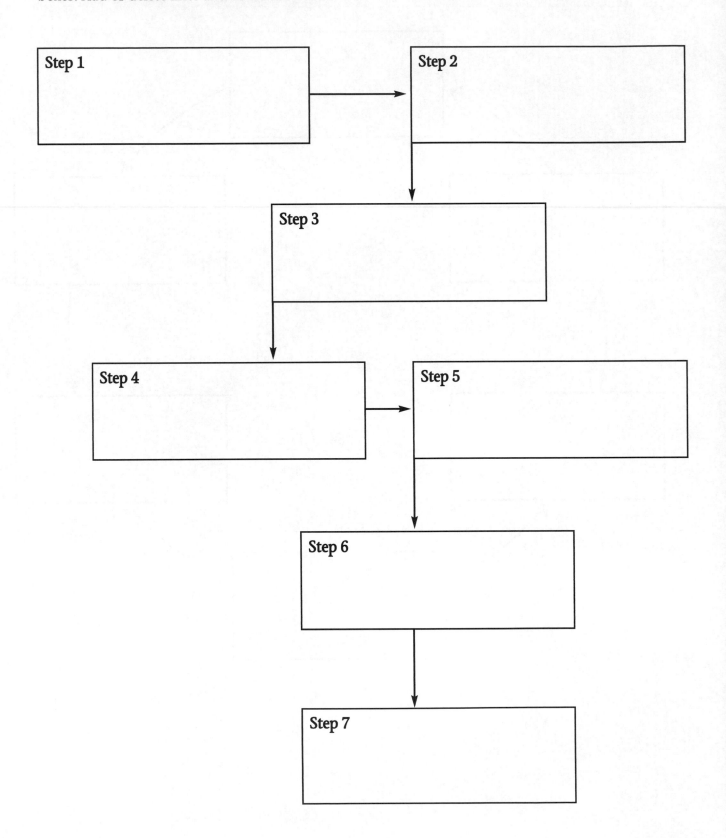

Teacher's Guide • Biology

A. Biology Words

In biology, special terms are often used. Knowing word parts can help you figure out unfamiliar words. You can add up the word parts to find the meaning of the whole word. For example, if you came across the word *epidermis,* you might not know what it meant. But if you saw that it combined the word parts *epi,* which means "outer," and *derm,* which means "skin," you might guess that it means "outer layer of skin."

Here are some word parts that are often combined to make biology words.

Word Part	Meaning	Example
a-, an-	without	anaerobic
aero-	air	aerobic
ambi-, amphi-	both	amphibian
anti-	against	antibiotic
archae-	ancient	archaebacteria
arthr-	joint	arthropod
auto-	self	autoimmune
bi-	two	bivalve
bio-	life	biology
co-	with	codominant
derm-	skin	dermis
di-	twice	diploid
eco-	environment	ecology
endo-	inside	endoderm
epi-	outer	epidermis
exo-	outside	exoskeleton
geo-	earth	geology
homo-	same	homologous
hydro-	water	hydrologic
meter	measure	thermometer
micro-	tiny	microscopic
mono-	one	monocot

Biology Words, *continued*

Word Part	Meaning	Example
morph-	shape, form	metamorphosis
neur-	nerve	neural
-ology	study, science	biology
-ose	carbohydrate	glucose
ova-, ovi-	egg	ovary
per-	through	permeable
photo-	light	photosynthesis
phys-	nature	physical
plat-	flat	platyhelminthes
-pod	foot	gastropod
poly-	many	polygenic
pro-, proto-	first	protist
pseudo-	apparent	pseudopod
-scop	look	microscope
sperm	seed	gymnosperm
sub-	under	subcutaneous
sym-, syn-	together, with	symbiosis
terr-	earth	terrarium
therm-	heat	thermometer
trans-	across	transpiration
trop-	turn	phototropism
-vore	eater	carnivore
zoo-	animal	zoology

B. The Parts of a Cell

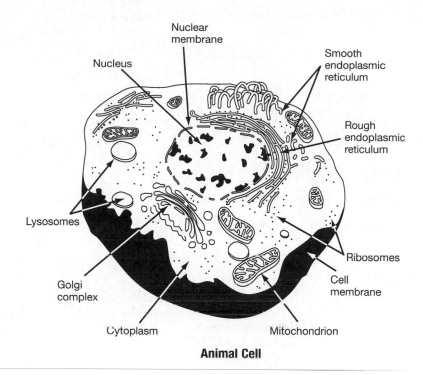

Animal Cell

Labels: Nuclear membrane, Nucleus, Smooth endoplasmic reticulum, Rough endoplasmic reticulum, Lysosomes, Ribosomes, Golgi complex, Cell membrane, Cytoplasm, Mitochondrion

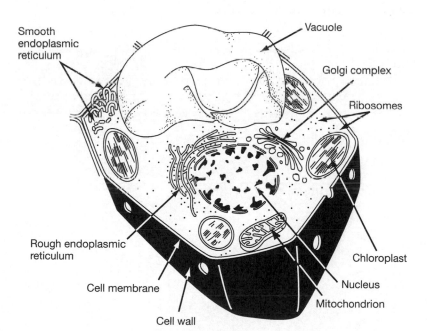

Plant Cell

Labels: Smooth endoplasmic reticulum, Vacuole, Golgi complex, Ribosomes, Rough endoplasmic reticulum, Chloroplast, Cell membrane, Nucleus, Cell wall, Mitochondrion

C. Classifying Living Things

The classification system used today includes six kingdoms: Animals, Plants, Archaebacteria, Eubacteria, Protists, and Fungi.

Animals

- Multicellular organisms that do not produce their own food but eat other organisms
- Include insects, fish, birds, mammals, mollusks, worms

Plants

- Organisms that have specialized cells, with cell walls
- Use chlorophyll and sunlight to make food by photosynthesis
- Include mosses, worts, lycopods, cone-bearing plants, flowering plants

Archaebacteria

- Single-celled organisms with no cell nucleus
- Most do not need oxygen

Eubacteria

- Single-celled organisms with no cell nucleus
- Some cause diseases such as Lyme disease
- Some, such as bacteria that turn milk into yogurt, are very useful

Protists

- Simple organisms with cell walls and nuclei
- Many are single-celled
- Some have many cells
- Include algae, protozoans, slime molds

Fungi

- Organisms that have cell walls, like plants, but do not photosynthesize
- Important decomposers
- Include mushrooms, molds, yeasts

Classifying Living Things, *continued*

The most common way to give the name of an organism is to list the name of the genus and the species. The name of the genus should be capitalized. The name of the species should be lowercase.

Kingdom

    Phylum/Division

        Class

            Order

                Family (Sub-Family)

                    Genus

                        Species (Subspecies)

D. The Parts of a Flowering Plant

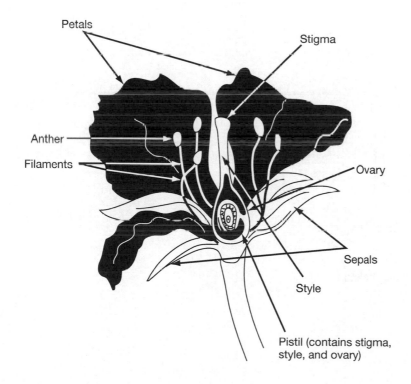

Petals

Stigma

Anther

Filaments

Ovary

Sepals

Style

Pistil (contains stigma, style, and ovary)

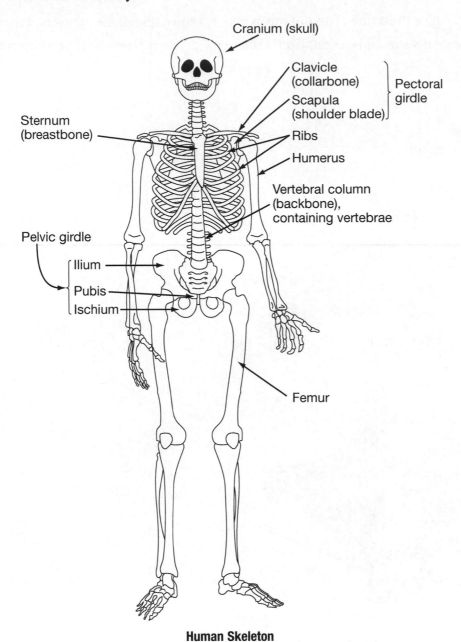

Human Skeleton

The Human Body, *continued*

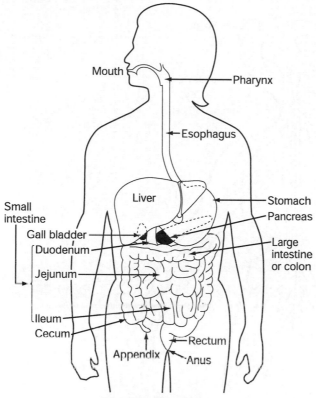

The Digestive System

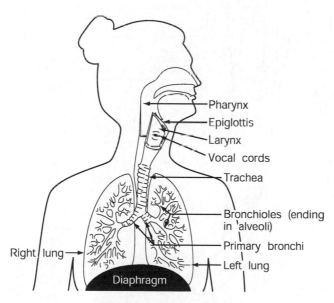

The Respiratory System

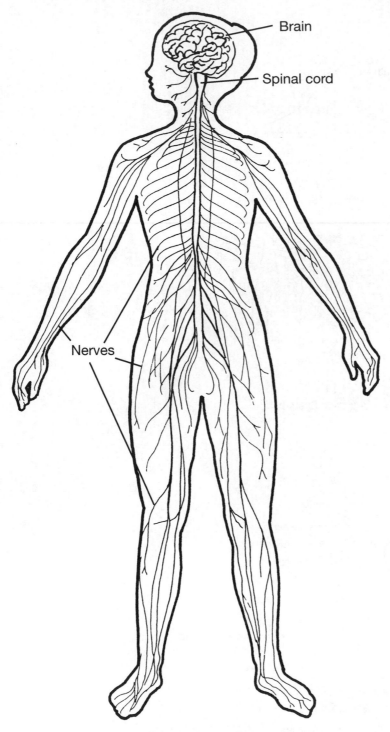

Brain

Spinal cord

Nerves

The Nervous System

The Human Body, *continued*

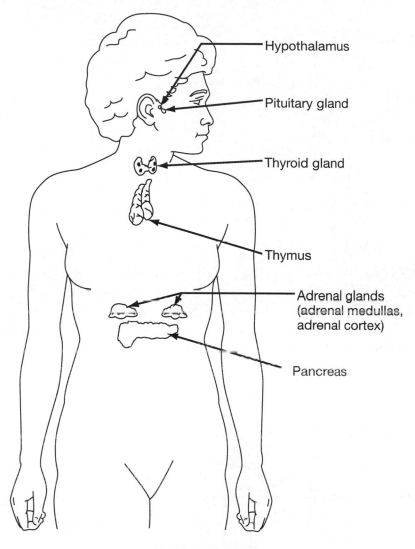

The Endocrine System

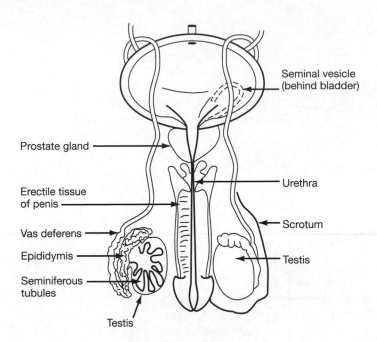

Seminal vesicle
(behind bladder)

Prostate gland

Erectile tissue
of penis

Urethra

Scrotum

Vas deferens

Epididymis

Testis

Seminiferous
tubules

Testis

Male Reproductive System

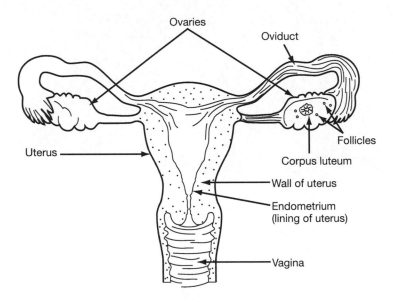

Ovaries

Oviduct

Follicles

Uterus

Corpus luteum

Wall of uterus

Endometrium
(lining of uterus)

Vagina

Female Reproductive System

The Human Body, *continued*

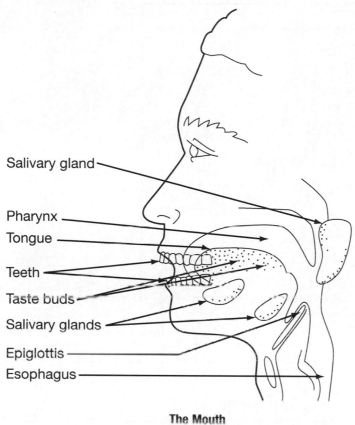

Salivary gland

Pharynx

Tongue

Teeth

Taste buds

Salivary glands

Epiglottis

Esophagus

The Mouth

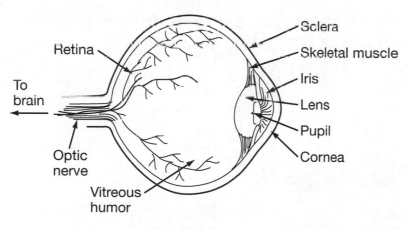

Retina

To brain

Optic nerve

Vitreous humor

Sclera

Skeletal muscle

Iris

Lens

Pupil

Cornea

The Eye

The Human Body, *continued*

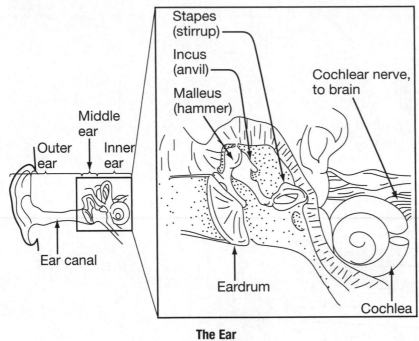

The Ear

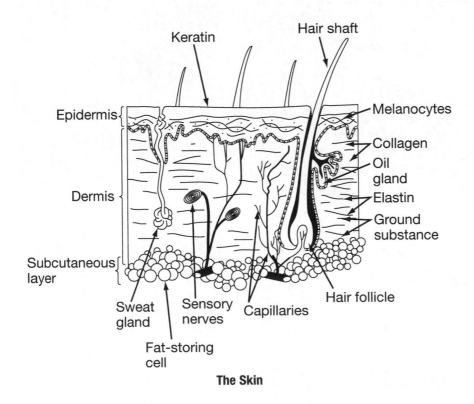

The Skin

Food Guide Pyramid
A Guide to Daily Food Choices

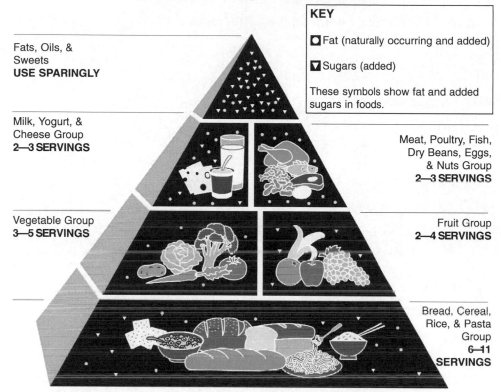

KEY

◻ Fat (naturally occurring and added)

▼ Sugars (added)

These symbols show fat and added sugars in foods.

Fats, Oils, & Sweets
USE SPARINGLY

Milk, Yogurt, & Cheese Group
2—3 SERVINGS

Meat, Poultry, Fish, Dry Beans, Eggs, & Nuts Group
2—3 SERVINGS

Vegetable Group
3—5 SERVINGS

Fruit Group
2—4 SERVINGS

Bread, Cereal, Rice, & Pasta Group
6—11 SERVINGS

Source: U.S. Department of Agriculture/U.S. Department of Health and Human Services

G. The Six Major Biomes
Tropical Rain Forests
Distribution

- in the tropics, near the equator
- South America: Amazon; Africa; India; Southeast Asia; Australia

Climate

- warm all year round
- average rainfall 250 centimeters per year
- two seasons: rainy and dry

Plants

- more plant species than all other biomes combined
- trees 25–35 meters tall, mostly evergreen
- orchids, bromeliads, vines (lianas), ferns, mosses, palms

Animals

antelopes	frogs	ocelots
bats	insects	spiders
birds	jaguars	snakes
deer	lizards	tapirs
elephants	monkeys	tigers

Threats

- deforestation

Deserts
Distribution

- hot and dry: Africa: Kalahari, Sahara, Namib; Australia: Great Sandy, Great Victoria, Simpson, Gibson, Tanami; North America: Mojave, Sonoran, Chihuahan, Great Basin; South America: Monte; South Asia: Thar; Southwest Asia: Arabian, Lut, Iranian
- semiarid: North America: Great Basin
- coastal: South America: Atacama
- cold: South America: Patagonian; Asia: Gobi, Turkestan; Antarctica: Antarctic

Climate

- very little rainfall
- climate can be hot and dry, semiarid, or cold

The Six Major Biomes, *continued*
Plants

- cactus
- spiny bushes and shrubs (agave, mesquite, prickly pear, yucca)

Animals

- antelopes, deer, gazelles
- armadillos
- bats
- birds (eagles, hawks, ostriches, owls, penguins, roadrunners, vultures)
- camels
- coyotes
- elephants
- foxes
- hyenas
- insects (beetles, scorpions)
- jackals
- jackrabbits
- kangaroos
- rabbits and hares
- reptiles (lizards, snakes, tortoises)
- rodents (gerbils, mice, rats, squirrels)
- spiders
- toads
- wolves

Grasslands

Distribution

- in middle latitudes, in interiors of continents
- South America: Argentina, Uruguay; Asia: Siberia; Africa (Kenya, Uganda, South Africa, Tanzania); Australia; India; Europe: Hungary; North America: Oklahoma, western Colorado (prairie)

Climate

- either moist continental or dry subtropical
- two seasons: growing season, dormant season
- rainfall concentrated in one part of the year, followed by period of drought
- two main divisions: savanna, steppe

The Six Major Biomes, *continued*

Plants

- grasses (buffalo grass, sagebrush, speargrass)
- small broad-leaved plants (asters, blazing stars, coneflowers, goldenrod, sunflowers, clover, indigo)
- occasional scattered trees (cottonwoods, oaks)

Animals

- antelopes
- badgers
- birds (blackbirds, grouse, hawks, larks, owls, quail, sparrows)
- bison
- cheetahs
- coyotes
- deer, elk, and gazelles
- elephants
- ferrets
- foxes
- giraffes
- hyenas
- insects (beetles, grasshoppers, termites)
- leopards
- lions
- moles
- mountain lions
- rabbits
- rodents (gophers, mice, prairie dogs, squirrels)
- snakes
- spiders
- wild horses
- wolves
- zebras

Threats

- overgrazing
- clearing for crops

The Six Major Biomes, *continued*
Deciduous Forests
Distribution

- eastern North America, northeastern Asia, western and central Europe

Climate

- moderate climate
- warm, wet summers; cold winters

Plants

- broad-leaved trees that drop their leaves in winter (ash, basswood, beech, cherry, elm, hemlock, hickory, maple, oak, willow)
- spring-flowering herbs
- ferns
- mosses

Animals

bears	foxes	rodents
birds	frogs	skunks
bobcats	insects	snakes
coyotes	mountain lions	turtles
deer	porcupines	weasels
fishers	rabbits	wolves

Taiga
Distribution

- between 50–60 degrees N: Siberia, Scandinavia, Alaska, Canada

Climate

- short, moist, moderately warm summers; long, cold, dry winters
- temperatures very low

Plants

- cold-tolerant evergreen conifers (pine, fir, spruce, tamarack)
- shrubs (blueberries)
- ground cover (moss, lichen)

Animals

- badgers
- bats
- bears (black bear, brown bear)

© 2005 Walch Publishing

The Six Major Biomes, *continued*

- beavers
- birds (eagles, finches, geese, hawks, sparrows, woodpeckers)
- bobcats
- caribou
- deer
- foxes
- hares
- insects (ants, blackflies, mosquitoes)
- lynx
- moose
- rabbits
- rodents (chipmunks, mice, squirrels, voles)
- sheep
- shrews
- weasels (ermine, martens, minks, wolverines)
- wolves

Threats

- logging

Tundra

Distribution

- in far north of Greenland, Alaska, Canada, Europe, Russia
- high on mountain slopes, above the tree line

Climate

- little rainfall; short, cool summers; long, cold winters
- cold, desertlike
- two types of tundra: Arctic tundra, alpine tundra
- in Arctic tundra, top layer of soil thaws in summer but deeper layer remains frozen

Plants

- low shrubs (blueberries, sedges)
- liverworts, grasses, lichens, mosses
- wildflowers (poppies, buttercups, saxifrage)
- tussock grasses
- dwarf trees

The Six Major Biomes, *continued*
Animals

- bears (grizzly, polar)
- birds (falcons, gulls, loons, ptarmigan, ravens, sandpipers, snow buntings, snow geese, snowy owls, terns, tundra swans)
- caribou
- elk
- fish (cod, flatfish, salmon, trout)
- foxes
- hares
- insects (butterflies, flies, grasshoppers, moths, mosquitoes)
- mountain goats
- musk oxen
- porcupines
- rodents (lemmings, squirrels, voles)
- sheep
- weasels (ermine, wolverines)
- wolves

GLOSSARY

abdomen (AB-duh-mun) the back part of the body of an arthropod, such as a spider or a crab

actin (AK-tun) long, ropelike protein found in skeletal muscles

active transport (AK-tiv TRANS-pohrt) movement of materials through a cell membrane using energy

adaptation (a-dap-TAY-shun) a change in an organism that helps it survive in its environment

adenine (A-dun-een) one of the bases that make up the genetic code of DNA and RNA

ADP (AY-DEE-PEE) (abbreviation for *adenosine diphosphate*) compound formed when ATP is broken down within a cell; can be used by a cell for energy

adrenal glands (uh-DREE-nul GLANDZ) glands located on the kidneys that produce the hormone adrenaline

adrenaline (uh-DRE-nul-un) hormone that increases heart rate and blood pressure; also called *epinephrine*

algae (AL-jee) plantlike protists that have chlorophyll and undergo photosynthesis; the singular form is *alga.*

algal bloom (AL-gul BLOOM) a dramatic increase in the number of algae in a body of water

allele (uh-LEEL) a form of a gene that determines alternate forms of a trait

allergies (A-lur-jees) overreactions of the immune system to substances (such as pollen or mold) that do not pose a threat to the body

alveoli (al-VEE-uh-ly) tiny air sacs in the lungs; the singular form is *alveolus.*

amino acids (uh-MEE-noh A-suds) long strings of chemical compounds that are used to make proteins

amniotic sac (am-nee-O-tik SAK) a fluid-filled sac that protects and nourishes the growing fetus of a bird, a reptile, or a mammal

amoebocytes (uh-MEE-buh-syts) jellylike cells in a sponge that carry food to other cells

amphibian (am-FI-bee-un) a coldblooded vertebrate (animal with a backbone) that lives part of its life in the water and part of its life on land

anaerobic (a-nuh-ROH-bik) unable to survive when oxygen is present

---

PRONUNCIATION KEY

CAPITAL LETTERS show the stressed syllables.

a as in mat	f as in fit	o as in cot, father	uh as in about, taken,
ay as in day, say	g as in go	oh as in go, note	lemon, pencil
ch as in chew	i as in sit	oo as in too	ur as in term
e as in bed	j as in job, gem	sh as in shy	y as in line, fly
ee as in even, easy,	k as in cool, key	th as in thin	zh as in vision,
need	ng as in running	u as in but, some	measure

anaphase (A-nuh-fayz) the third stage of mitosis in which the chromosomes split and move to opposite ends of the cell

ancestor (AN-ses-tur) an earlier organism from which an individual or group has developed

annelids (A-nul-udz) worms with segmented bodies; they include marine worms, earthworms, and leeches.

antennae (an-TE-nee) slender, jointed sensory organs on the head of some arthropods, such as insects

anthers (AN-thurz) the parts at the tip of a plant's stamen that contain pollen

antibiotics (an-ti-by-O-tiks) medicines that kill disease-causing bacteria

antibodies (AN-ti-bo-deez) substances that act against specific pathogens

anticodons (an-ti-KOH-donz) group of three nucleotides that bind to codons on mRNA during protein synthesis

antigen (AN-ti-jun) a substance that causes the immune system to respond

antioxidants (an-tee-OK-suh-dunts) substances, such as vitamins C and E, that bind to and deactivate harmful chemicals in the body

antiserums (AN-tee-sir-ums) serums that contain antibodies against specific pathogens

anus (AY-nus) the opening at the end of the digestive system through which solid wastes are eliminated

aorta (ay-OR-tuh) the main blood vessel that carries blood from the heart

appendicular skeleton (a-pun-DI-kyuh-lur   SKE-luh-tun) the bones of the upper and lower limbs, including the shoulders, collarbones, hips, arms, legs, and feet

appendix (uh-PEN-diks) a fingerlike structure in the large intestine that serves no function in the body

arachnids (uh-RAK-nuds) a large class of arthropods (invertebrates with jointed limbs) that includes spiders, scorpions, mites, and ticks

archaebacteria (ar-kee-bak-TIR-ee-uh) a kingdom of single-celled organisms with no cell nucleus; most live in very harsh environments.

arteries (AR-tuh-rees) blood vessels that carry blood from the heart to the rest of the body

arterioles (ar-TIR-ee-olz) small blood vessels that branch off from the arteries

---

PRONUNCIATION KEY

CAPITAL LETTERS show the stressed syllables.

a	as in mat	f	as in fit	o	as in cot, father	uh	as in about, taken,
ay	as in day, say	g	as in go	oh	as in go, note		lemon, pencil
ch	as in chew	i	as in sit	oo	as in too	ur	as in term
e	as in bed	j	as in job, gem	sh	as in shy	y	as in line, fly
ee	as in even, easy,	k	as in cool, key	th	as in thin	zh	as in vision,
	need	ng	as in running	u	as in but, some		measure

arthropods (AR-thruh-podz) invertebrates (animals without backbones) that have segmented bodies and jointed limbs; includes insects, spiders, ticks, and crabs

astrocytes (AS-truh-syts) star-shaped cells in the central nervous system

atmospheric pressure (at-muh-SFIR-ik   PRE-shur) the normal pressure created by gas molecules (such as oxygen and carbon dioxide) in the air

atoms (A-tumz) the smallest parts of an element that have all the chemical properties of the element

ATP (AY-TEE-PEE) (abbreviation for *adenosine triphosphate*) a compound, found in living cells, that can store and release energy

atrium (AY-tree-um) a chamber of a mammal's heart that receives blood from the veins; the plural form is *atria*.

autoimmune diseases (aw-toh-im-YOON   di-ZEEZ-ez) diseases in which the immune system mistakenly attacks the body's own cells

autonomic nervous system (aw-tuh-NO-mik   NER-vus   SIS-tum) the part of the nervous system that controls things we are not aware of or cannot control, such as the release of hormones

autosome (AW-tuh-sohm) a chromosome that determines all body features

axial skeleton (AK-see-ul   SKE-luh-tun) the part of the skeleton that includes the skull, spinal column, ribs, and breastbone

axons (AK-sonz) fibers on nerve cells that carry nerve impulses away from the cell

bacilli (buh-SI-lee) rod-shaped bacteria; the singular form is *bacillus*.

bacteria (bak-TIR-ee-uh) single-celled organisms that have no cell nucleus; the singular form is *bacterium*.

B-cells (BEE-selz) lymphocytes manufactured in bone marrow that recognize and/or destroy a specific type of pathogen

behavioral adaptation (bi-HAY-vyuh-rul   a-dap-TAY-shun) a change in the way an organism acts, or behaves

bile (BYL) a liquid produced in the liver that aids in the digestion of fats

binary fission (BY-nuh-ree   FI-shun) reproduction by splitting in two to produce two identical cells

binding sites (BYND-ing   SYTS) places on the ends of amino acid chains that latch on to the antigens on the surface of pathogens

---

PRONUNCIATION KEY

CAPITAL LETTERS show the stressed syllables.

a as in mat	f as in fit	o as in cot, father	uh as in about, taken, lemon, pencil
ay as in day, say	g as in go	oh as in go, note	
ch as in chew	i as in sit	oo as in too	ur as in term
e as in bed	j as in job, gem	sh as in shy	y as in line, fly
ee as in even, easy, need	k as in cool, key	th as in thin	zh as in vision, measure
	ng as in running	u as in but, some	

biome (BY-ohm) any one of six major ecosystems that has a characteristic climate and kinds of organisms

bivalves (BY-valvz) mollusks, such as clams and scallops, that have two hinged shells

bladder (BLA-dur) the part of the body that stores urine

blastocyst (BLAS-tuh-sist) an embryo when it is a hollow ball of cells

blastoderm (BLAS-tuh-durm) a disk-shaped mass of cells inside the blastocyst that is the part that will turn into the baby

blood-brain barrier (BLUD-BRAYN BAR-ee-ur) the intensive screening process substances must go through to enter the brain

bony fish (BOH-nee FISH) fish with skeletons made of bones

Bowman's capsule (BOH-munz CAP-sul) a structure at the end of a nephron that contains a knot of blood vessels

bronchi (BRON-ky) tubes that lead from the trachea to the lungs; the singular form is *bronchus.*

bronchioles (BRON-kee-ohlz) small tubes that branch from the secondary bronchi

bud (BUD) a tightly packed bundle at the end of a twig on a tree in the spring that opens up into a leaf

calcium gate (KAL-see-um GAYT) point at which calcium enters the axon

cambium (KAM-bee-um) a layer of growth tissue inside a tree trunk

camouflage (KA-muh-flozh) a method that animals use to protect themselves from predators in which they blend into the background of their environment

capillaries (KA-puh-ler-eez) tiny blood vessels that connect arteries to veins

carapace (KAR-uh-pays) the protective shield that covers the body of a crustacean

carbohydrates (kar-boh-HY-drayts) starches and sugars

carbon (KAR-bun) element that forms the basis for living tissue

carbon dioxide (KAR-bun dy-OK-syd) the form of carbon when it is in the air

carbonic acid (kar-BO-nik A-sud) an acid formed when the carbon dioxide released during respiration reacts with water

cardiac muscle (KAR-dee-ak MUH-sul) the muscle that makes up the heart

---

PRONUNCIATION KEY

CAPITAL LETTERS show the stressed syllables.

a	as in m**a**t	f	as in **f**it	o	as in c**o**t, f**a**ther	uh	as in **a**bout, tak**e**n, lem**o**n, penc**i**l
ay	as in d**ay**, s**ay**	g	as in **g**o	oh	as in g**o**, n**o**te	ur	as in t**er**m
ch	as in **ch**ew	i	as in s**i**t	oo	as in t**oo**	y	as in l**i**ne, fl**y**
e	as in b**e**d	j	as in **j**ob, **g**em	sh	as in **sh**y	zh	as in vi**s**ion, mea**s**ure
ee	as in **e**ven, **ea**sy, n**ee**d	k	as in **c**ool, **k**ey	th	as in **th**in		
		ng	as in runni**ng**	u	as in b**u**t, s**o**me		

carnivore (KAR-nuh-vohr) an animal that eats other animals

cartilage (KAR-tul-ij) a strong connective tissue that is lighter and more flexible than bone

cartilaginous fish (kar-tuh-LA-juh-nus FISH) fish that have skeletons made of cartilage

cecum (SEE-kum) the first part of the large intestine

cell wall (SEL WOL) a rigid barrier that surrounds the cells of organisms such as plants, algae, and fungi

cells (SELZ) the basic units of all living things

cellulose (SEL-yoo-lohs) carbohydrates woven together to make up the cell wall in plants, algae, and fungi

central nervous system (SEN-trul NER-vus SIS-tum) the part of the nervous system where processing takes place; includes the brain and the spinal cord

centriole (SEN-tree-ohl) a structure at each pole of a cell

cephalopods (SE-fuh-luh-pods) mollusks with no outer shell; includes squid and octopuses

cephalothorax (se-fuh-luh-THOHR-aks) the front section of the body where the head and thorax are combined in some anthropods, such as spiders and crustaceans

cerebellum (ser-uh-BE-lum) the part of the brain that controls coordination and balance

cerebral cortex (suh-REE-brul KOR-teks) the wrinkled gray matter on top of the cerebrum, which is composed of tightly packed dendrites and cell bodies

cerebrum (suh-REE-brum) the part of the brain that controls most voluntary thought and actions

chelicerae (ki-LI-suh-ree) clawlike mouthparts of some arthropods, such as spiders

chelicerates (ki-LI-suh-rayts) class of arthropods that includes arachnids

chemoreceptors (kee-moh-ri-SEP-turz) sensory nerves that detect specific chemicals

chitin (KY-tun) a hard but flexible substance found in the exoskeleton of arthropods; in the cell walls of fungi; and in the fingernails, claws, and hair of mammals

chlorophyll (KLOHR-uh-fil) a plant substance, usually green, that absorbs light energy for use in photosynthesis

chloroplasts (KLOHR-uh-plasts) the part of a plant where photosynthesis is carried out

choanocytes (KOH-a-nuh-syts) group of cells lining the inside cavity of a sponge

---

PRONUNCIATION KEY

CAPITAL LETTERS show the stressed syllables.

a	as in mat	f	as in fit	o	as in cot, father	uh	as in about, taken, lemon, pencil
ay	as in day, say	g	as in go	oh	as in go, note		
ch	as in chew	i	as in sit	oo	as in too	ur	as in term
e	as in bed	j	as in job, gem	sh	as in shy	y	as in line, fly
ee	as in even, easy, need	k	as in cool, key	th	as in thin	zh	as in vision, measure
		ng	as in running	u	as in but, some		

chordates (KOR-dayts) organisms that, at some stage of development, have gill slits, a central nerve cord, and a flexible rod of cells forming a support along the back

chorion (KOHR-ee-on) a structure that combines with the endometrium to form the placenta

chromatid (KROH-muh-tud) each copy of the chromosome that results from the prophase of mitosis

chromatin (KROH-muh-tun) the combination of histones and DNA

chromosomes (KROH-muh-sohmz) bundles of coiled DNA inside the nucleus

chyme (KYM) partly digested food that passes from the stomach to the small intestine

cilia (SI-lee-uh) tiny, hairlike projections; the singular form is *cilium.*

class (KLAS) group of related orders of organisms; division of a phylum

classification (kla-suh-fuh-KAY-shun) a system of grouping organisms based on similar features

classify (kla-suh-FY) to group together

closed circulatory system (KLOHZD   SUR-kyuh-luh-tohr-ee   SIS-tum) a system that pumps blood through veins in an endless loop

cnidarian (ny-DAR-ee-un) invertebrate with a hollow body and tentacles with stinging cells; occurs in two forms, polyp and medusa; includes jellyfish, anemones, and corals

cocci (KO-kee) round or oval eubacteria; the singular form is *coccus.*

cochlea (KOH-klee-uh) a coiled structure in the inner ear that receives sound waves

codominance (koh-DO-muh-nuns) in heredity, when two genes are present for a trait and neither one is either dominant or recessive

codons (KOH-dons) three-letter sequences in the mRNA molecule

coeloms (SEE-lums) fluid-filled hollow spaces in an animal's body that contain the digestive organs

coenzymes (koh-EN-zymz) vitamins that activate enzymes by binding to them and changing their shape

coldblooded (KOHLD-BLUH-dud) unable to control body temperature from inside, but taking on the temperature of the outside air or water

collagen (KO-luh-jun) a tough, fibrous protein that makes up most of the dermis and gives skin its strength

collecting duct (kuh-LEK-ting   DUKT) a duct that runs through the medulla to the ureter through which water may passively flow

---

PRONUNCIATION KEY

CAPITAL LETTERS show the stressed syllables.

a as in m**a**t	f as in f**i**t	o as in c**o**t, f**a**ther	uh as in **a**bout, tak**e**n,
ay as in d**ay**, s**ay**	g as in **g**o	oh as in g**o**, n**o**te	lem**o**n, penc**i**l
ch as in **ch**ew	i as in s**i**t	oo as in t**oo**	ur as in t**er**m
e as in b**e**d	j as in **j**ob, **g**em	sh as in **sh**y	y as in l**i**ne, fl**y**
ee as in **e**ven, **ea**sy,	k as in **c**ool, **k**ey	th as in **th**in	zh as in vi**s**ion,
n**ee**d	ng as in runni**ng**	u as in b**u**t, s**o**me	m**ea**sure

colon (KOH-lun) part of the large intestine

commensalism (kuh-MEN-suh-li-zum) a relationship in which one species benefits while the second species does not benefit, but is not harmed

community (kuh-MYOO-nuh-tee) made up of all the organisms that live in one area

compact bone (kum-PAKT BOHN) the hardest part of a bone

competition (kom-puh-TI-shun) the struggle between organisms for resources such as food, water, and light

cones (KOHNZ) parts of the eye that detect color

conifers (KO-nuh-furz) cone-bearing trees, such as pines or firs

cornea (KOR-nee-uh) the clear, curved covering through which light enters the eye

coronary arteries (KOR-uh-ner-ee AR-tuh-rees) arteries that provide blood for the heart

corpus luteum (KOR-pus LOO-tee-um) a hormone-producing structure that forms in the ovary after a mature egg is released

cortex (KOR-teks) structure on the kidney that contains filtering structures

cortisol (KOR-tuh-sol) a hormone that stimulates the body to convert amino acids and fats into glucose

cranium (KRAY-nee-um) the skull; part of the axial skeleton

crossing over (KROS-ing OH-vur) the exchange of DNA in prophase I

crustaceans (krus-TAY-shuns) mostly water-dwelling arthropods that have a hard outer covering; includes lobsters, crabs, and shrimp

cytoplasm (SY-tuh-pla-zum) a jellylike material in most cells that surrounds the nucleus

cytosine (SY-tuh-seen) one of the bases that make up the genetic code of DNA and RNA

dark phase (DARK FAYZ) second phase of photosynthesis, during which light is not needed

daughter cells (DO-tur SELZ) cells produced by division of the parent cell that are identical copies of the parent

deciduous forests (di-SI-juh-wus FOR-usts) ecosystem found in areas with warm, wet summers and cold winters in which trees drop their leaves in winter

decomposers (dee-kum-POH-zurz) organisms, such as bacteria and fungi, that break down dead organic matter

---

PRONUNCIATION KEY

CAPITAL LETTERS show the stressed syllables.

a as in mat	f as in fit	o as in cot, father	uh as in about, taken,
ay as in day, say	g as in go	oh as in go, note	lemon, pencil
ch as in chew	i as in sit	oo as in too	ur as in term
e as in bed	j as in job, gem	sh as in shy	y as in line, fly
ee as in even, easy,	k as in cool, key	th as in thin	zh as in vision,
need	ng as in running	u as in but, some	measure

Teacher's Guide • Biology

dendrites (DEN-dryts) short, branching extensions of nerve cells that receive information from stimuli or from other nerve cells

deoxyribose (dee-ok-si-RY-bohs) a five-carbon sugar found in DNA

depolarization (dee-poh-luh-ruh-ZAY-shun) process by which the inside of a cell becomes more positively charged than the outside of the cell

dermis (DUR-mus) a thick layer of skin under the epidermis

desert (DE-zurt) a biome that usually receives less than 25 centimeters of rain each year

diaphragm (DY-uh-fram) a sheet of muscles under the lungs that aids in breathing

diastolic pressure (dy-uh-STO-lik PRE-shur) the pressure of the blood in the veins between heartbeats; the second number in a blood pressure reading, such as 120/80

dicot (DY-kot) a plant whose seeds have two seed leaves

diffusion (di-FYOO-zhun) the movement of molecules from an area of higher concentration to an area of lower concentration

digestive tract (di-JES-tiv TRAKT) the system that breaks food down into nutrients that the body can use

diploid cells (DY-ployd SELZ) cells that contain two sets of chromosomes, with one set from each parent

disk (DISK) a small, circular cushion between the bones of the spine

division (duh-VI-zhun) the second-highest level of classification for plants, between kingdom and class

DNA (DEE-EN-AY) the molecules in a cell that contain genetic information that determines the structure and function of the cell; abbreviation for *deoxyribonucleic acid*

DNA polymerase (DEE-EN-AY PO-luh-muh-rays) an enzyme that unwinds the double helix of DNA molecules during mitosis

dominant (DO-muh-nunt) a gene or trait that always shows itself

double helix (DU-bul HEE-liks) the twisted, ladderlike shape of two DNA strands wrapped around each other

duodenum (doo-uh-DEE-num) the first section of the small intestine

ear canal (IR kuh-NAL) a narrow chamber of the ear through which sound waves enter

---

ecologist (i-KO-luh-jist) a person who studies how living things interact

ecology (i-KO-luh-jee) the study of interactions among living things

ecosystem (EE-koh-sis-tum) the plants, animals, and nonliving things that make up a community and its environment, and the relationships between these living and nonliving things

ectoderm (EK-tuh-durm) the outer layer of cells in an embryo that will develop into the skin and nervous system

effectors (i-FEK-turz) tissues that become active in response to nerve impulses

egg (EG) the female reproductive cell

ejaculation (i-ja-kyuh-LAY-shun) the discharge of sperm from the male penis

elastin (i-LAS-tun) a protein that helps skin go back to its normal shape after it has been stretched

element (E-luh-munt) one of the fundamental substances, such as oxygen and carbon, that can be combined to make up all matter; each element contains atoms of only one kind.

embryo (EM-bree-oh) the early stage of growth of a plant or an animal after an egg is fertilized

endocrine system (EN-duh-krun   SIS-tum) the system of glands and hormones that helps regulate other body systems, such as heart rate and glucose levels in the blood

endoderm (EN-duh-durm) the inner layer of cells in an embryo that will develop into the digestive and respiratory systems

endometrium (en-doh-MEE-tree-um) the thick, blood-rich lining of the uterus during ovulation

endoplasmic reticulum (ER) (en-duh-PLAZ-mik   ri-TI-kyuh-lum) (EE-AR) a network of folded membranes within the cell that manufactures and stores many chemicals

energy (E-nur-jee) the ability to do work

enzymes (EN-zymz) proteins produced by living cells that can speed up or slow down biological reactions such as the digestion of food

epidermis (e-puh-DUR-mus) the outermost layer of skin

epiglottis (e-puh-GLO-tus) a flap of tissue that keeps food and liquids from entering the windpipe

epinephrine (e-puh-NE-frun) a hormone produced by the adrenal glands that provides you with a surge of energy

epiphytes (E-puh-fyts) plants that grow in trees instead of soil

---

PRONUNCIATION KEY

CAPITAL LETTERS show the stressed syllables.

a	as in m**a**t	f	as in **f**it	o	as in c**o**t, f**a**ther	uh	as in **a**bout, tak**e**n,
ay	as in d**ay**, s**ay**	g	as in **g**o	oh	as in g**o**, n**o**te		lem**o**n, penc**i**l
ch	as in **ch**ew	i	as in s**i**t	oo	as in t**oo**	ur	as in t**er**m
e	as in b**e**d	j	as in **j**ob, **g**em	sh	as in **sh**y	y	as in l**i**ne, fl**y**
ee	as in **e**ven, **ea**sy,	k	as in **c**ool, **k**ey	th	as in **th**in	zh	as in vi**s**ion,
	n**ee**d	ng	as in runni**ng**	u	as in b**u**t, s**o**me		mea**s**ure

esophagus (i-SO-fuh-guhs) the tube that moves food from the mouth to the stomach

essential amino acids (i-SEN-shul uh-MEE-noh A-suds) amino acids that are necessary for growth but that cannot be made in the body and so must be obtained from food

estrogen (ES-truh-jun) a female sex hormone that triggers the development of secondary sex characteristics, such as the development of breasts and the widening of the hips

eubacteria (yoo-bak-TIR-ee-uh) single-celled organisms with no cell nucleus that are more complex than archaebacteria

eukaryote (yoo-KAR-ee-oht) a cell that has a nucleus

evaporation (i-va-puh-RAY-shun) changing from a liquid to a gas

evolution (e-vuh-LOO-shun) the gradual change in organisms over time

exoskeleton (ek-soh-SKE-luh-tun) a hard outer covering found around the body of some invertebrates such as insects

extinct (ik-STINKT) no longer existing

fallopian tube (fuh-LOH-pee-un TOOB) a tube in mammals through which the egg travels from an ovary to the uterus

family (FAM-lee) in classification, a grouping of related genera; a subdivision of order

fat-soluble (FAT-SOL-yuh-bul) needing fats to be digested, absorbed, and carried through the body

feces (FEE-seez) solid waste material left over at the end of the digestive process, which is expelled from the body

ferns (FURNZ) vascular plants, with leaflike fronds, that reproduce by spores

fertilization (fur-tul-uh-ZAY-shun) the joining of male and female reproductive cells

fetus (FEE-tus) a developing young mammal in the uterus

fibers (FY-burs) specialized cells that make up muscles

fibroblasts (FY-bruh-blasts) cells found in connective tissue that secrete collagen and elastin

fibrous root system (FY-brus ROOT SIS-tum) a root system made up of many stringy roots that cling to the soil

filaments (FI-luh-munts) 1. the threadlike chains of cells that make up fungi; 2. the thin parts of a plant's stamen that support the pollen-containing anthers

---

PRONUNCIATION KEY

CAPITAL LETTERS show the stressed syllables.

a as in m**a**t	f as in **f**it	o as in c**o**t, f**a**ther	uh as in **a**bout, tak**e**n,
ay as in d**ay**, s**ay**	g as in **g**o	oh as in g**o**, n**o**te	lem**o**n, penc**i**l
ch as in **ch**ew	i as in s**i**t	oo as in t**oo**	ur as in t**er**m
e as in b**e**d	j as in **j**ob, **g**em	sh as in **sh**y	y as in l**i**ne, fl**y**
ee as in **e**ven, **ea**sy,	k as in **c**ool, **k**ey	th as in **th**in	zh as in vi**s**ion,
n**ee**d	ng as in runni**ng**	u as in b**u**t, s**o**me	mea**s**ure

first order consumer (FIRST OR-dur kon-SOO-mur) animal that eats only plants

fitness (FIT-nus) an individual's ability to reproduce and pass on its genes

flagella (fluh-JE-luh) whiplike structures that move simple organisms around; the singular form is *flagellum.*

follicle (FA-li-kul) a small sac or pore, such as those in the skin from which hairs grow, and those in the ovary where eggs develop

follicle stimulating hormone (FSH) (FA-li-kul STIM-yuh-lay-ting HOR-mohn) (EF-ES-AYCH) a hormone released by the pituitary gland that triggers ovulation in females and sperm production in males

food chain (FOOD CHAYN) a series of organisms in which each organism uses the next one as a food source

food pyramid (FOOD PIR-uh-mid) 1. guideline prepared by the USDA that shows the number of servings of different kinds of foods you should get every day; 2. a pyramid-shaped diagram that shows food relationships among organisms in an ecosystem; the chief predator appears at the top of the pyramid and each level preys on the level below, with plants on the bottom level.

food web (FOOD WEB) all the possible feeding relationships in an ecosystem

fossil record (FO-sul RE-kurd) the traces of ancient organisms that are preserved in earth and rock and that help scientists understand when different organisms were alive, where they lived, and what they looked like

fronds (FRONDZ) large, feathery leaves

frontal lobe (FRUN-tul LOHB) the part of the cerebrum at the front of the head, responsible for speech, movement, emotional control, and thinking processes such as problem solving and decision making

fungi (FUN-jy) organisms that have cell walls and do not produce chlorophyll; examples: mushrooms, molds, yeast; the singular form is *fungus.*

gallbladder (GOL-bla-dur) a small organ that stores bile

gametes (GA-meets) sex cells

gastropods (GAS-truh-podz) mollusks with a muscular foot and either a single shell or no shell at all; include snails and slugs

---

PRONUNCIATION KEY

CAPITAL LETTERS show the stressed syllables.

a as in mat	f as in fit	o as in cot, father	uh as in about, taken,
ay as in day, say	g as in go	oh as in go, note	lemon, pencil
ch as in chew	i as in sit	oo as in too	ur as in term
e as in bed	j as in job, gem	sh as in shy	y as in line, fly
ee as in even, easy,	k as in cool, key	th as in thin	zh as in vision,
need	ng as in running	u as in but, some	measure

gastrulation (gas-truh-LAY-shun) process in the development of the embryo during which cells in the blastoderm develop differences and form layers

gene (JEEN) a factor that controls inherited traits

gene pool (JEEN POOL) the sum of all the genes in a population

genotype (JEE-nuh-typ) the genetic makeup of an individual organism

genus (JEE-nus) in classification, a group of related species; subdivision of family

geotropism (JEE-uh-troh-pi-zum) the tendency for plant roots to move downward in response to gravity

germinate (JUR-muh-nayt) start to grow

gill slits (GIL SLITS) structures in water-dwelling organisms that filter food and oxygen from the water

gills (GILZ) organs that filter food and oxygen from water

glands (GLANDZ) organs that make chemical substances such as sweat and bile that are used or released by the body

glial cells (GLEE-ul SELZ) cells that support and protect nerve cells in the brain

glomerulus (gluh-MER-uh-lus) a knot of blood vessels inside the Bowman's capsules of the kidney

glucagon (GLOO-kuh-gon) one of two hormones that control sugar levels in the blood

glucose (GLOO-kohs) a sugar that is an important source of energy in plants and animals

glycogen (GLY-kuh-jun) the form in which glucose is stored in the liver and muscles

Golgi complex (GOL-jee KOM-pleks) a series of flattened sacs within a cell where materials are modified and distributed to other parts of the cell

gram-negative (GRAM-NE-guh-tiv) refers to bacteria that do not react to a certain dye

gram-positive (GRAM-PO-zuh-tiv) refers to bacteria that react to a certain dye by turning purple

grassland (GRAS-land) an ecosystem in which grasses are the most common plant and few trees or shrubs are found

greenhouse effect (GREEN-haus i-FEKT) the warming effect on Earth's atmosphere created when carbon dioxide and other gases trap heat in the atmosphere

ground substance (GROWND SUB-stunts) a gel-like substance that fills the spaces between cells and proteins in the skin

---

PRONUNCIATION KEY

CAPITAL LETTERS show the stressed syllables.

a	as in m**a**t	f	as in **f**it	o	as in c**o**t, f**a**ther	uh	as in **a**bout, tak**e**n,
ay	as in d**ay**, s**ay**	g	as in **g**o	oh	as in g**o**, n**o**te		lem**o**n, penc**i**l
ch	as in **ch**ew	i	as in s**i**t	oo	as in t**oo**	ur	as in t**er**m
e	as in b**e**d	j	as in **j**ob, **g**em	sh	as in **sh**y	y	as in l**i**ne, fl**y**
ee	as in **e**ven, **ea**sy,	k	as in **c**ool, **k**ey	th	as in **th**in	zh	as in vi**s**ion,
	n**ee**d	ng	as in runni**ng**	u	as in b**u**t, s**o**me		mea**s**ure

growth hormone (GROHTH   HOR-mohn) a chemical in plants or animals that regulates growth

guanine (GWO-neen) one of the bases that make up the genetic code of DNA and RNA

gymnosperms (JIM-nuh-spurmz) plants that produce uncovered seeds such as pine cones

habitat (HA-buh-tat) the type of place where an organism usually lives

hair (HAYR) a slender, threadlike growth made up mostly of keratin

haploid cells (HA-ploid   SELZ) cells with only one set of chromosomes; usually sex cells

Haversian canal (huh-VUR-zhun   kuh-NAL) thin canal within bone tissue that carries nutrients and oxygen

Haversian systems (huh-VUR-zhun   SIS-tums) in compact bone, tightly stacked rods that contain layers of minerals and collagen

heart (HART) the organ that pumps to move blood through the circulatory system

hemisphere (HE-muh-sfir) one of the two halves of the cerebrum

hemocoels (HEE-muh-seelz) in arthropods and mollusks, the spaces between the organs that blood flows through

hemoglobin (HEE-muh-gloh-bun) the part of red blood cells that can carry oxygen

herbivore (UR-buh-vohr) an animal that eats plants

herbivory (ur-BI-vuh-ree) eating plants

heredity (her-ED-i-tee) the passing on of characteristics from parent to offspring

heterozygous (he-tuh-roh-ZY-gus) having two different forms of a gene for the same trait, one from each parent

hindbrain (HYND-brayn) the part of the brain behind the spinal cord that includes the cerebellum and the medulla

histamine (HIS-tuh-meen) a chemical released by white blood cells and damaged skin cells that causes blood vessels to dilate

histones (HIS-tohns) proteins that help package DNA into chromosomes

homologous (hoh-MO-luh-gus) similar in appearance and structure, but not necessarily having the same function

homozygous (hoh-muh-ZY-gus) having two like genes for the same trait

---

PRONUNCIATION KEY

CAPITAL LETTERS show the stressed syllables.

a	as in m**a**t	f	as in **f**it	o	as in c**o**t, f**a**ther	uh	as in **a**bout, tak**e**n,
ay	as in d**ay**, s**ay**	g	as in **g**o	oh	as in g**o**, n**o**te		lem**o**n, penc**i**l
ch	as in **ch**ew	i	as in s**i**t	oo	as in t**oo**	ur	as in t**er**m
e	as in b**e**d	j	as in **j**ob, **g**em	sh	as in **sh**y	y	as in l**i**ne, fl**y**
ee	as in **e**ven, **ea**sy,	k	as in **c**ool, **k**ey	th	as in **th**in	zh	as in vi**s**ion,
	n**ee**d	ng	as in runni**ng**	u	as in b**u**t, s**o**me		mea**s**ure

hormones (HOR-mohnz) chemical messengers that are produced in one part of an organism and affect another part

horsetails (HORS-taylz) ancient vascular plants that look like reeds with evenly spaced joints along the stem

hydrochloric acid (hy-druh-KLOHR-ik   A-sud) a powerful acid (molecular formula HCl) secreted in the stomach that starts the chemical digestion process

hydrotropism (hy-DRO-truh-pi-zum) plant movement in response to water

hypha (HY-fuh) a long, threadlike chain of cells that is the basic structure of the fungus; the plural form is *hyphae.*

hypothalamus (hy-poh-THA-luh-mus) area of the brain above the pituitary gland that secretes hormones and regulates heart rate, blood pressure, body temperature, and appetite

ileum (I-lee-um) part of the small intestine

immune (i-MYOON) resistant to, not affected by

immune system (i-MYOON   SIS-tum) the system that protects the body against foreign substances and things that might cause disease

impermeable (im-PUR-mee-uh-bul) unable to be penetrated

incus (IN-kus) one of the tiny bones in the middle ear; also called the *anvil*

inhibin (in-HI-bun) a hormone that stops the production of follicle-stimulating hormone, or FSH

inhibitors (in-HI-buh-turz) molecules that prevent chemical reactions in a muscle that is in a relaxed state

insects (IN-sekts) small, six-legged invertebrates whose bodies are divided into three distinct parts

insulin (IN-suh-lun) a chemical produced in the pancreas that controls blood sugar levels

interferons (in-tuh-FIR-onz) proteins secreted when cells are infected by a virus that protect other cells from the virus

interphase (IN-tur-fayz) growth period of a cell during which the chromosomes are duplicated

interspecific competition (in-tur-spi-SI-fik   kom-puh-TI-shun) competition between individuals of different species

intraspecific competition (in-truh-spi-SI-fik   kom-puh-TI-shun) competition between individuals of the same species

---

PRONUNCIATION KEY

CAPITAL LETTERS show the stressed syllables.

a	as in m**a**t	f	as in **f**it	o	as in c**o**t, f**a**ther	uh	as in **a**bout, tak**e**n,
ay	as in d**ay**, s**ay**	g	as in **g**o	oh	as in g**o**, n**o**te		lem**o**n, penc**i**l
ch	as in **ch**ew	i	as in s**i**t	oo	as in t**oo**	ur	as in t**er**m
e	as in b**e**d	j	as in **j**ob, **g**em	sh	as in **sh**y	y	as in l**i**ne, fl**y**
ee	as in **e**ven, **ea**sy,	k	as in **c**ool, **k**ey	th	as in **th**in	zh	as in vi**s**ion,
	n**ee**d	ng	as in runni**ng**	u	as in b**u**t, s**o**me		mea**s**ure

invertebrate (in-VUR-tuh-brut) an animal that has no backbone

ion (Y-un) an atom that has either a positive charge or a negative charge

iris (Y-rus) the colored part of the eye that controls the size of the pupil

jawless fish (JO-lus   FISH) a group of fish that do not have true jaws; they usually eat by suction.

jejunum (ji-JOO-num) a section of the small intestine

joints (JOINTS) places in the body where two or more bones meet; for example, knees, elbows, hips

keratin (KER-uh-tun) a protein that makes up human hair and fingernails and the top layer of human skin

kidneys (KID-neez) organs that remove impurities from the blood

kingdom (KING-dum) in classification, the most general of the seven levels

large intestine (LARJ   in-TES-tun) the lower part of the digestive system, which receives a soupy mix of digested food from the small intestine, absorbs most of the fluids, and passes the remaining material out of the body through the anus

larvae (LAR-vee) organisms at an immature stage of development in which they look different from the adult form; the singular form is *larva*.

larynx (LAR-inks) the boxlike entrance to the windpipe that contains the vocal cords

leaves (LEEVZ) the parts of plants that grow from a stem or twig and make food by photosynthesis; the singular form is *leaf.*

legumes (LE-gyooms) plants, such as alfalfa and soybeans, that have bacteria in their roots that convert nitrogen to a form the plant can use, thus adding nitrogen to the soil

lens (LENZ) the transparent, flexible part of the eye that focuses light entering the eye

lichen (LY-kun) a symbiotic relationship between an alga and a fungus

ligaments (LI-guh-munts) strong, flexible cords made of collagen that hold bones together at joints

light phase (LYT   FAYZ) the stage of photosynthesis that is driven by energy from the sun

limbic system (LIM-bik   SIS-tum) structures in the brain that control emotions

lipase (LY-pays) an enzyme produced by the pancreas that breaks fats down as part of the digestive process

lipids (LI-puds) fats and oils

PRONUNCIATION KEY

CAPITAL LETTERS show the stressed syllables.

a as in m**a**t	f as in **f**it	o as in c**o**t, f**a**ther	uh as in **a**bout, tak**e**n,
ay as in d**ay**, s**ay**	g as in **g**o	oh as in g**o**, n**o**te	lem**o**n, penc**i**l
ch as in **ch**ew	i as in s**i**t	oo as in t**oo**	ur as in t**er**m
e as in b**e**d	j as in **j**ob, **g**em	sh as in **sh**y	y as in l**i**ne, fl**y**
ee as in **e**ven, **ea**sy,	k as in **c**ool, **k**ey	th as in **th**in	zh as in vi**s**ion,
n**ee**d	ng as in runni**ng**	u as in b**u**t, s**o**me	mea**s**ure

liver (LI-vur) a large organ that converts sugar to glycogen; removes and stores excess cholesterol; and produces bile, which is used to digest fat

loop of Henle (LOOP   UV   HEN-lee) U-shaped section in the kidney that helps adjust the concentration of water in urine

luteinizing hormone (LH) (LOO-tee-uh-ny-zing   HOR-mohn) a hormone that stimulates ovulation in females and sperm production in males

lycopod (LY-cuh-pod) primitive evergreen mosslike plant that uses spores to reproduce

lymph (LIMF) a clear fluid that contains white blood cells and circulates through the body, removing bacteria and certain proteins from tissues and transporting fat from the small intestines

lymph nodes (LIMF   NOHDZ) nodes that filter particles from lymph and produce and house cells of the immune system

lymphatic system (lim-FA-tik   SIS-tum) a network of vessels that returns fluid lost by the blood to the circulatory system

lymphocytes (LIM-fuh-syts) disease-fighting white blood cells

lysosomes (LY-suh-sohmz) enzyme-containing cell parts that help digest food and break down old cell parts

M phase (EM   FAYZ) stage of the cell cycle when cell division takes place; the M stands for mitosis.

macrophage (MA-kruh-fayj) phagocyte cell of the immune system that destroys pathogens and toxins and displays their antigens

malleus (MA-lee-us) tiny, outermost bone in the middle ear, also known as the *hammer*

maltose (MOL-tohs) a sugar formed when digestive enzymes begin to break down starch

mammal (MA-mul) a warmblooded, highly developed vertebrate that has body hair and produces milk to feed its young

mammary glands (MA-muh-ree   GLANDZ) glands in female mammals that produce milk

mantle (MAN-tul) the thin sheet of tissue in mollusks that surrounds the internal organs and usually creates a shell

marrow (MAR-oh) the soft tissue inside bones; yellow marrow is high in fat and red marrow makes blood cells.

marsupial (mar-SOO-pee-ul) a mammal that gives birth to undeveloped embryos, which are then carried in an exterior pouch until they are ready to survive on their own

---

PRONUNCIATION KEY

CAPITAL LETTERS show the stressed syllables.

a as in m**a**t	f as in **f**it	o as in c**o**t, f**a**ther	uh as in **a**bout, tak**e**n,
ay as in d**ay**, s**ay**	g as in **g**o	oh as in g**o**, n**o**te	lem**o**n, penc**i**l
ch as in **ch**ew	i as in s**i**t	oo as in t**oo**	ur as in t**er**m
e as in b**e**d	j as in **j**ob, **g**em	sh as in **sh**y	y as in l**i**ne, fl**y**
ee as in **e**ven, **ea**sy,	k as in **c**ool, **k**ey	th as in **th**in	zh as in vi**s**ion,
n**ee**d	ng as in runni**ng**	u as in b**u**t, s**o**me	mea**s**ure

mast cells (MAST SELZ) phagocytes that help stimulate the immune response when the skin gets injured

medulla (muh-DUH-luh) part of the brain that controls involuntary functions

medusa (mi-DOO-suh) the umbrella-shaped, free-swimming stage of some cnidarians

meiosis (mee-OH-sus) cell division process that creates sex cells

meiotic interphase (mee-O-tik IN-tur-fayz) the period between meiosis I and meiosis II in the cell division process

melanin (ME-luh-nun) pigment that gives skin its color and protects the skin from harmful ultraviolet radiation from the sun

membrane (MEM-brayn) a thin, flexible sheet or layer

meninges (muh-NIN-jeez) three protective membranes inside the skull

menstrual cycle (MEN-stroo-ul SY-kul) the four-week cycle during which an oocyte matures into an egg and travels to the uterus, and the blood-rich endometrium is then shed

mesoderm (ME-zuh-durm) the middle layer of cells in an embryo that will develop into the skeletal, muscular, and circulatory systems

mesoglea (me-zuh-GLEE-uh) fluidlike substance in a cnidarian that acts like a skeleton, giving the animal its shape

messenger RNA (mRNA) and (ME-sun-jur AR-EN-AY) type of RNA involved in protein synthesis

metabolism (mu-TA-buh-li-zum) the rate at which cells produce chemical changes in substances, creating energy

metamorphosis (me-tuh-MOR-fuh-sus) a change in body type or structure during life, as with a caterpillar becoming a butterfly

metaphase (ME-tuh-fayz) second stage of mitosis or meiosis in which spindles arrange the chromosomes in the middle of the cell

microscopic (my-kruh-SKO-pik) able to be seen only when magnified by a microscope

mimicry (MI-mi-kree) resemblance of one living thing to another or to natural objects that gives an advantage, such as protection from predators

mitochondria (my-tuh-KON-dree-uh) round or rod-shaped structures in a cell in which food molecules are broken down to produce energy; the singular form is *mitochondrion*.

PRONUNCIATION KEY

CAPITAL LETTERS show the stressed syllables.

a	as in m**a**t	f	as in **f**it	o	as in c**o**t, f**a**ther	uh	as in **a**bout, tak**e**n,
ay	as in d**ay**, s**ay**	g	as in **g**o	oh	as in g**o**, n**o**te		lem**o**n, penc**i**l
ch	as in **ch**ew	i	as in s**i**t	oo	as in t**oo**	ur	as in t**er**m
e	as in b**e**d	j	as in **j**ob, **g**em	sh	as in **sh**y	y	as in l**i**ne, fl**y**
ee	as in **e**ven, **ea**sy,	k	as in **c**ool, **k**ey	th	as in **th**in	zh	as in vi**s**ion,
	n**ee**d	ng	as in runni**ng**	u	as in b**u**t, s**o**me		mea**s**ure

mitosis (my-TOH-sus) cell division process during which chromosomes are equally distributed to the two daughter cells

molecules (MO-li-kyoolz) a group of two or more atoms held together by a bond

mollusks (MO-lusks) soft-bodied invertebrates that usually have a shell

molting (MOL-ting) process in which a creature sheds its outer covering, hair, shell, feathers, or horns, which are then replaced with new growth

monocot (MO-nuh-kot) a flowering plant with one seed leaf in each seed

motor cortex (MOH-tur   KOR-teks) region of the brain's frontal lobe that controls voluntary muscle movement

mucous membrane (MYOO-kus   MEM-brayn) tissue that lines the inside of the nasal passages

mucus (MYOO-kus) slippery substance produced by mucous membranes to moisten and protect body areas; also produced by snails and slugs to slide along on top of

muscles (MUH-sulz) tissues that are attached to the bones and aid in movement, assist organs in their work, or are part of the heart

muscular foot (MUHS-kyuh-lur   FUT) strong appendage used by many mollusks to move, to grip surfaces, and to dig into the ground

mutagens (MYOO-tuh-junz) agents that cause mutations

mutate (MYOO-tayt) to go through mutation

mutation (myoo-TAY-shun) a physical change in a chromosome or a chemical change in a gene that is inherited

mutualism (MYOO-chuh-wuh-li-zum) relationship between different kinds of organisms in which both organisms benefit

mycelium (my-SEE-lee-um) in fungi, an interwoven mat made up of branching hyphae

myelin sheath (MY-uh-lun   SHEETH) a fatty layer that surrounds some nerve fibers

myosin (MY-uh-sun) long, ropelike proteins in muscles

myosin heads (MY-uh-sun   HEDZ) a series of extensions, or ratchets, on strands of myosin

natural selection (NA-chuh-rul   suh-LEK-shun) changes in populations that occur when organisms with favorable variations for a particular environment survive and pass on those variations

nectar (NEK-tur) sweet liquid produced by flowers to entice insects, birds, and bats to pollinate them

---

PRONUNCIATION KEY

CAPITAL LETTERS show the stressed syllables.

a as in m**a**t	f as in **f**it	o as in c**o**t, f**a**ther	uh as in **a**bout, tak**e**n,
ay as in d**ay**, s**ay**	g as in **g**o	oh as in **go**, n**o**te	lem**o**n, penc**i**l
ch as in **ch**ew	i as in s**i**t	oo as in t**oo**	ur as in t**er**m
e as in b**e**d	j as in **j**ob, **g**em	sh as in **sh**y	y as in l**i**ne, fl**y**
ee as in **e**ven, **ea**sy,	k as in **c**ool, **k**ey	th as in **th**in	zh as in vi**s**ion,
n**ee**d	ng as in runni**ng**	u as in b**u**t, s**o**me	mea**s**ure

nematodes (NE-muh-tohdz) invertebrate phylum that includes all roundworms

nephrons (NE-fronz) tiny structures in the kidneys that filter wastes from the blood

nervous system (NER-vus   SIS-tum) body system that includes the brain, spinal cord, and all peripheral nerves

neurons (NOO-ronz) tightly wound bundles of cells that make up nerves

neurotransmitters (nur-oh-trans-MI-turs) substances that transmit nerve impulses across a synaptic gap

niche (neesh) the part an organism plays in an ecological community

nitrogen-containing base (NY-truh-jun-kun-TAYN-ing   BAYS) DNA base that is composed of one or two rings of nitrogen and carbon

nodes (NOHDZ) a distinct mass of one kind of tissue enclosed in tissue of a different kind

nodes of Ranvier (NOHDZ   UV   RON-vee-ay) nodes of nerve fibers; impulses jump from node to node to allow for a fast transfer of nervous information

nondisjunction (non-dis-JUNK-shun) failure of chromosomes to separate properly

nonvascular plants (non-VAS-kyuh-lur   PLANTS) plants that cannot store and transport water

norepinephrine (NOR-e-puh-NE-frun) a neurotransmitter, and an energy-producing hormone in the adrenal glands

notochord (NOH-tuh-kord) a strong but flexible rod of cells found under the nerve cord; in vertebrates, the structure from which the backbone develops

nuclear envelope (NOO-klee-ur   EN-vuh-lohp) the membrane that surrounds the nucleus

nucleic acids (nu-KLEE-ik   A-sudz) complex organic acids that form nucleotide chains; the major ones are DNA and RNA, and contain an organism's basic genetic information

nucleoid (NOO-klee-oid) a region of cytoplasm where the cell's DNA is found

nucleoli (noo-KLEE-uh-ly) organelles within the nucleus where ribosomal RNA is produced; the singular form is *nucleolus.*

nucleotides (NOO-klee-uh-tydz) long chains of compounds that are the basic structural units of nucleic acids

nucleus (NOO-klee-us) the part of a cell that controls many of the functions of the cell and contains the organism's DNA

PRONUNCIATION KEY

CAPITAL LETTERS show the stressed syllables.

a	as in m**a**t	f	as in **f**it	o	as in c**o**t, f**a**ther	uh	as in **a**bout, tak**e**n,
ay	as in d**ay**, s**ay**	g	as in **g**o	oh	as in g**o**, n**o**te		lem**o**n, penc**i**l
ch	as in **ch**ew	i	as in s**i**t	oo	as in t**oo**	ur	as in t**er**m
e	as in b**e**d	j	as in **j**ob, **g**em	sh	as in **sh**y	y	as in l**i**ne, fl**y**
ee	as in **e**ven, **ea**sy,	k	as in **c**ool, **k**ey	th	as in **th**in	zh	as in vi**s**ion,
	n**ee**d	ng	as in runni**ng**	u	as in b**u**t, s**o**me		mea**s**ure

occipital lobe (ok-SI-puh-tul LOHB) section at the back of the brain that processes visual information

offspring (OF-spring) new organisms produced by living things

omnivore (OM-ni-vohr) a consumer that eats both plants and animals

oogenesis (oh-uh-JE-nuh-sus) the process by which eggs are formed and mature

oogonia (oh-uh-GOH-nee-uh) diploid cells that begin the process of meiosis in the developing fetus

optic nerve (OP-tik NURV) bundle of neurons that carries visual information from the retina of the eye to the brain

order (OR-dur) in classification, a group of related families

organ (OR-gan) group of specialized tissues that perform an activity together

organelles (or-guh-NELZ) small structures inside cells that have specialized functions

organic molecules (or-GA-nik MO-li-kyoolz) large molecules made up mostly of carbon atoms that are unique to living things and make life possible

organism (OR-guh-ni-zum) a living thing

osmosis (oz-MOH-sus) movement of water across a semipermeable membrane from a high concentration to a low concentration

osteocytes (OS-tee-uh-syts) cells that maintain compact bones by synthesizing collagen and assembling minerals

ovaries (OH-vuh-rees) female reproductive organs

oviduct (OH-vuh-dukt) tube through which the egg cell travels from an ovary to the uterus in mammals

ovulation (ov-yuh-LAY-shun) the release of a mature egg cell from an ovary

pacemaker (PAYS-may-kur) a node in the right atrium of the heart that sends signals that establish and maintain a steady heartbeat

pancreas (PAN-kree-us) a large gland that produces digestive enzymes and the hormones insulin and glucagon

parasites (PAR-uh-syts) organisms that live in, on, or with other organisms, usually gaining benefits while causing harm to the hosts

---

PRONUNCIATION KEY

CAPITAL LETTERS show the stressed syllables.

a	as in m**a**t	f	as in **f**it	o	as in c**o**t, f**a**ther	uh	as in **a**bout, tak**e**n, lem**o**n, penc**i**l
ay	as in d**ay**, s**ay**	g	as in **g**o	oh	as in g**o**, n**o**te		
ch	as in **ch**ew	i	as in s**i**t	oo	as in t**oo**	ur	as in t**er**m
e	as in b**e**d	j	as in **j**ob, **g**em	sh	as in **sh**y	y	as in l**i**ne, fl**y**
ee	as in **e**ven, **ea**sy, n**ee**d	k	as in **c**ool, **k**ey	th	as in **th**in	zh	as in vi**s**ion, mea**s**ure
		ng	as in runni**ng**	u	as in b**u**t, s**o**me		

parasitism (PAR-uh-suh-ti-zum) a close association between two organisms in which a parasite benefits while harming the host

parietal lobe (puh-RY-uh-tul   LOHB) section of the brain that processes nerve impulses related to body sensations; it helps maintain balance.

partial pressure (PAR-shul   PRE-shur) the pressure exerted by each individual gas in a mixture of gases

passive transport (PA-siv   trans-POHRT) the movement of molecules across a cell membrane without use of energy by the cell

pathogens (PA-thuh-junz) organisms that invade the bodies of larger organisms and cause disease

pectoral girdle (PEK-tuh-rul   GUR-dul) the arch of bones or cartilage that supports the forelimbs of a vertebrate

pedipalps (PE-duh-palps) second pair of mouthparts on an arachnid

pelvic girdle (PEL-vik   GUR-dul) the arch of bones or cartilage that supports the hind limbs of a vertebrate

penis (PEE-nus) the male sex organ through which sperm flow

pepsin (PEP-sun) a protein-cutting enzyme produced in the stomach

peripheral nervous system (per-I-fur-al   NER-vus   SIS-tum) all nerves in the human body except the brain and spinal cord

peristalsis (per-uh-STOL-sus) waves of involuntary, coordinated muscle contractions during the process of digestion

permeable (PUR-mee-uh-bul) able to allow fluids and particles to pass through

petals (PE-tulz) leaflike flower parts, often brightly colored or perfumed

phagocytes (FA-guh-syts) cells such as white blood cells that engulf and consume foreign materials such as invading bacteria and debris

pharynx (FAR-inks) a muscular tube in vertebrates that extends from the back of the mouth and nasal cavity to the esophagus; air and food pass through it.

phenotype (FEE-nuh-typ) a trait that you can see on an individual organism

phloem (FLOH-em) tissue in the roots, stems, and leaves of higher plants that carries dissolved food through tubes from those parts to other parts of the plant

---

PRONUNCIATION KEY

CAPITAL LETTERS show the stressed syllables.

a as in m**a**t	f as in **f**it	o as in c**o**t, f**a**ther	uh as in **a**bout, tak**e**n,
ay as in d**ay**, s**ay**	g as in **g**o	oh as in g**o**, n**o**te	lem**o**n, penc**i**l
ch as in **ch**ew	i as in s**i**t	oo as in t**oo**	ur as in t**er**m
e as in b**e**d	j as in **j**ob, **g**em	sh as in **sh**y	y as in l**i**ne, fl**y**
ee as in **e**ven, **ea**sy,	k as in **c**ool, **k**ey	th as in **th**in	zh as in vi**s**ion,
n**ee**d	ng as in runni**ng**	u as in b**u**t, s**o**me	mea**s**ure

phosphate (FOS-fayt) an organic compound made up of a phosphorus atom surrounded by three oxygen atoms

photosynthesis (foh-toh-SIN-thuh-sus) a process in which plants and some other organisms use energy from the sun to convert water and carbon dioxide to food

phototropism (foh-TO-truh-pi-zum) plant movement in response to light

phylum (FY-lum) a level of classification below kingdom; the broadest group within each kingdom

physical adaptation (FI-zi-kul   a-dap-TAY-shun) a physical change in an organism that helps it survive in a particular environment

pistil (PIS-tul) female part of a flower

pituitary gland (puh-TOO-uh-ter-ee   GLAND) gland in the human brain that secretes growth hormones and reproductive hormones

placenta (pluh-SEN-tuh) organ developed during pregnancy that supplies the fetus or embryo with food, water, and oxygen

placental (pluh-SEN-tul) a mammal that is fully developed at birth

plasmodium (plaz-MOH-dee-um) a community of slime molds

platelets (PLAYT-luts) tiny disks in mammals' blood that helps blood to clot

platyhelminthes (pla-ti-HEL-min-theez) invertebrate phylum that includes flatworms such as tapeworms

polarization (poh-luh-ruh-ZAY-shun) the process by which the inside of a cell becomes more negatively charged than the outside of the cell

pollen (PO-lun) microspores in a seed plant that appear as a fine yellow dust and contain the male reproductive cells of the plant

pollination (po-luh-NAY-shun) the transfer of pollen from the anther to the stigma

polygenic traits (po-lee-JEE-nik   TRAYTS) traits that are determined by more than one gene

polyp (PO-lup) an invertebrate that has a hollow, tubelike body

population (po-pyuh-LAY-shun) a group of organisms of the same species living in one area

pores (POHRS) tiny openings in animals or plants, especially those that allow matter to pass through a membrane

poriferan (poh-RIF-ur-un) invertebrate phylum containing sponges

---

PRONUNCIATION KEY

CAPITAL LETTERS show the stressed syllables.

a	as in m**a**t	f	as in **f**it	o	as in c**o**t, f**a**ther	uh	as in **a**bout, tak**e**n,
ay	as in d**ay**, s**ay**	g	as in **g**o	oh	as in g**o**, n**o**te		lem**o**n, penc**i**l
ch	as in **ch**ew	i	as in s**i**t	oo	as in t**oo**	ur	as in t**er**m
e	as in b**e**d	j	as in **j**ob, **g**em	sh	as in **sh**y	y	as in l**i**ne, fl**y**
ee	as in **e**ven, **ea**sy,	k	as in **c**ool, **k**ey	th	as in **th**in	zh	as in vi**s**ion,
	n**ee**d	ng	as in runni**ng**	u	as in b**u**t, s**o**me		mea**s**ure

precipitation (pri-si-puh-TAY-shun) water that falls to earth as rain, snow, sleet, hail, or mist

predation (pri-DAY-shun) the act of hunting or killing for food

predator (PRE-duh-tur) an animal that hunts and kills another organism for food

prefrontal area (pree-FRUN-tul AR-ee-uh) area at the front of the brain's frontal lobe that sorts out all the sensory information your occipital and temporal lobes receive and places it into context

prey (PRAY) an organism that is hunted and killed by another organism for food

primary consumers (PRY-mer-ee kun-SOO-murz) organisms that get their energy by eating producers

primary oocytes (PRY-mer-ee OH-uh-syts) immature eggs that remain in prophase I for years

producers (pruh-DOO-surz) organisms that use the sun's energy to convert carbon dioxide into a simple sugar called glucose

progesterone (proh-JES-tuh-rohn) a female sex hormone that stimulates changes in the uterus so it will accept a fertilized egg and nourish the developing embryo

prokaryote (proh-KAR-ee-oht) a cell that does not have a nucleus

prolactin (proh-LAK-tun) a pituitary hormone that triggers the mammary glands in the mother's breasts to produce milk

prophase (PROH-fayz) the first stage of mitosis, in which the nucleus begins to change greatly; also the first stage of meiosis, in which chromosomes become visible under a microscope

prostate gland (PROS-tayt GLAND) doughnut-shaped gland in males that produces semen, the fluid that transports sperm

prothallus (proh-THA-lus) the gametophyte generation in ferns and other spore-bearing plants

protist (PROH-tist) simple organism with cell walls and nuclei; many are single-celled, but some have many cells.

protozoans (proh-tuh-ZOH-unz) protists that behave very much like animals in many ways

pseudocoelom (soo-duh-SEE-lum) cavity, or hollow place, in roundworms outside the digestive tract, filled with fluid that helps cushion the digestive tract and also acts as a skeleton

pseudopod (SOO-doh-pod) temporary cytoplasm "feet" used by amoebas for movement and catching prey

puberty (PYOO-bur-tee) the period during which young mammals become sexually mature

---

PRONUNCIATION KEY

CAPITAL LETTERS show the stressed syllables.

a	as in m**a**t	f	as in **f**it	o	as in c**o**t, f**a**ther	uh	as in **a**bout, tak**e**n,
ay	as in d**ay**, s**ay**	g	as in **g**o	oh	as in g**o**, n**o**te		lem**o**n, penc**i**l
ch	as in **ch**ew	i	as in s**i**t	oo	as in t**oo**	ur	as in t**er**m
e	as in b**e**d	j	as in **j**ob, **g**em	sh	as in **sh**y	y	as in l**i**ne, fl**y**
ee	as in **e**ven, **ea**sy,	k	as in **c**ool, **k**ey	th	as in **th**in	zh	as in vi**s**ion,
	n**ee**d	ng	as in runni**ng**	u	as in b**u**t, s**o**me		mea**s**ure

pulmonary (PUL-muh-ner-ee) relating to the lungs

pulmonary artery (PUL-muh-ner-ee AR-tuh-ree) artery that brings venous blood (oxygen-depleted blood from the veins) from the heart to the lungs

pulmonary veins (PUL-muh-ner-ee VAYNZ) veins that return oxygen-rich blood from the lungs to the heart

Punnett square (PUH-nut SKWAYR) a chart used to calculate possible gene combinations

pupa (PYOO-puh) the stage of metamorphosis from which the larva emerges as an adult

pupil (PYOO-pul) the opening in the iris of the eye that lets light in

purebred (PUR-bred) organisms with ancestry that does not contain hybrids

recessive (ree-SES-iv) a gene that is not expressed in the offspring

rain forest (RAYN FOR-ust) a tropical, wet biome

rectum (REK-tum) final segment of the digestive system; passes feces out of the body through the anus

red blood cells (RED BLUD SELZ) reddish cells of the blood that contain hemoglobin and deliver oxygen from the lungs to the body's tissues

relaxin (ri-LAK-sun) sex hormone that loosens joints in the mother's pelvis so that the baby can pass out of the birth canal

renal artery (REE-nul AR-tuh-ree) large blood vessel that brings blood in need of filtering to a kidney

renal pelvis (REE-nul PEL-vus) hollow area in the center of a kidney where urine is temporarily stored

renal vein (REE-nul VAYN) vein through which cleansed blood leaves a kidney

reproduction (ree-pruh-DUK-shun) the way in which organisms produce offspring

reptile (REP-tyl) coldblooded, air-breathing vertebrate that lays amniotic eggs

resource partitioning (REE-sohrs par-TI-shun-ing) the situation when organisms live in the same geographic area and consume slightly different foods or use resources in slightly different ways

respiration (res-puh-RAY-shun) the process of taking in oxygen and releasing carbon dioxide

resting state (RES-ting STAYT) the state of a neuron when an impulse is not traveling along an axon

retina (RE-tun-uh) a stamp-sized patch at the back of the eyeball that detects light

---

PRONUNCIATION KEY

CAPITAL LETTERS show the stressed syllables.

a	as in mat	f	as in fit	o	as in cot, father	uh	as in about, taken,
ay	as in day, say	g	as in go	oh	as in go, note		lemon, pencil
ch	as in chew	i	as in sit	oo	as in too	ur	as in term
e	as in bed	j	as in job, gem	sh	as in shy	y	as in line, fly
ee	as in even, easy,	k	as in cool, key	th	as in thin	zh	as in vision,
	need	ng	as in running	u	as in but, some		measure

rhizomes (RY-zohmz) underground stems of some plants

ribonucleic acid (RNA) (ry-boh-nu-KLEE-ik A-sud) (AR-EN-AY) any of various nucleic acids that contain ribose and are associated with protein synthesis

ribose (RY-bohs) a five-carbon sugar found in RNA nucleotides

ribosomal RNA (rRNA) (ry-buh-SOH-mul AR-EN-AY) RNA that is a fundamental element of the structure of ribosomes

ribosomes (RY-buh-sohmz) tiny structures that make proteins for the cells

RNA polymerase (AR-EN-AY PO-luh-muh-rays) an enzyme active in the synthesis of RNA

rods (RODS) light receptors in the retina that are most sensitive to dim light

roots (ROOTS) 1. underground organs in plants that absorb water and nutrients and transport them to the stem of the plant; 2. the part of the tooth that contains nerves and blood vessels

saliva (suh-LY-vuh) moisture in the mouth that begins the digestive process

salivary glands (SA-luh-ver-ee GLANDZ) three glands in the mouth that produce saliva

sarcomere (SAR-kuh-mir) a part of the muscle fiber between stripes of actin fibers

sarcoplasmic reticula (sar-kuh-PLAZ-mik ri-TI-kyuh-luh) a structure within muscle fibers that stores calcium

schwann cells (SHWON SELZ) fatty membranes that make up the sheath around some nerve cells, protecting the cells and acting as electric insulators

sclera (SKLER-uh) a tough white membrane that covers most of the eyeball

scrotum (SKROH-tum) a sac that hangs outside the male body and contains the testes

sebum (SEE-bum) an oily substance produced by hair follicles that lubricates the skin

secondary consumers (SE-kun-der-ee kun-SOO-murz) organisms that get their energy by eating primary consumers; meat eaters

secondary sexual characteristics (SE-kun-der-ee SEK-shuh-wul kar-ik-tuh-RIS-tiks) characteristics caused by an influx of sex hormones, such as growth of facial hair in males and breast development in females

secrete (si-KREET) to produce a substance within a cell, a gland, or an organ and release it

semen (SEE-mun) sperm-containing fluid produced by males

seminal vesicles (SE-muh-nul VE-si-kulz) two glands in males that produce semen

---

PRONUNCIATION KEY

CAPITAL LETTERS show the stressed syllables.

a as in mat	f as in fit	o as in cot, father	uh as in about, taken,
ay as in day, say	g as in go	oh as in go, note	lemon, pencil
ch as in chew	i as in sit	oo as in too	ur as in term
e as in bed	j as in job, gem	sh as in shy	y as in line, fly
ee as in even, easy,	k as in cool, key	th as in thin	zh as in vision,
need	ng as in running	u as in but, some	measure

semipermeable (se-mee-PUR-mee-uh-bul) able to allow some fluids and particles to pass through, but not others

sense organs (SENS OR-gunz) organs used to detect changes in the outside world, such as an insect's antennae and a human's eyes and ears

sensory neurons (SENS-ree NOO-ronz) neurons that detect stimuli such as light, sound, heat, or pressure

sensory receptors (SENS-ree ri-SEP-turz) organs and nerves that translate a stimulus into an electric impulse that can be used by the brain to interpret the stimulus

sepals (SEE-pulz) a circle of green petals at the base of a flower

sertoli cells (sur-TOH-lee SELZ) cells that provide the spermatozoa with nutrients

serum proteins (SIR-um PROH-teenz) an assembly of amino acids that compose the liquid part of the blood

sex cells (SEKS SELZ) gametes, or cells that can be used in reproduction; in humans, the sperm and the egg

sex-linked (SEKS-LINKD) any trait located on the X chromosome; usually carried by the female and expressed in the male; recessive

sexual reproduction (SEK-shuh-wul ree-pruh-DUK-shun) reproduction that involves two organisms of the same species, each contributing genetic information to the offspring

shaft (SHAFT) the middle area of long bones such as the humerus, which forms a hollow ring that contains spongy bone tissue such as marrow

shell (SHEL) a hard outer covering for invertebrates such as mollusks

sister chromatids (SIS-tur KROH-muh-tudz) two chromosomes that bind with each other during cellular reproduction

skeletal muscles (SKE-luh-tul MUH-sulz) muscles attached to the skeleton by cartilage

skeleton (SKE-luh-tun) the internal support system of vertebrates, composed of bone or cartilage

skin (SKIN) the external covering of some vertebrates that protects the organism from infection and is an important sensory organ

smooth muscles (SMOOTH MUH-sulz) muscles in organs and the circulatory system that move mostly through involuntary action such as breathing, digestion, and circulation

solvent (SOL-vunt) any substance that can dissolve another substance, such as water

---

PRONUNCIATION KEY

CAPITAL LETTERS show the stressed syllables.

a	as in mat	f	as in fit	o	as in cot, father	uh	as in about, taken,
ay	as in day, say	g	as in go	oh	as in go, note		lemon, pencil
ch	as in chew	i	as in sit	oo	as in too	ur	as in term
e	as in bed	j	as in job, gem	sh	as in shy	y	as in line, fly
ee	as in even, easy,	k	as in cool, key	th	as in thin	zh	as in vision,
	need	ng	as in running	u	as in but, some		measure

somatic nervous system (soh-MA-tik   NER-vus   SIS-tum) the nervous system that controls sensations that an animal is aware of, such as pain, light, and sound, and the voluntary movement of muscles

specialize (SPE-shuh-lyz) the tendency of organisms to evolve toward using specialized food sources, light requirements, and soil nutrients

speciation (spee-shee-AY-shun) a change in populations that occurs when two populations that would normally breed together are isolated

species (SPEE-sheez) any group of organisms that can breed together and produce fertile offspring; in classification, the smallest group of organisms

sperm (SPURM) male sex cell

spermatids (SPUR-muh-tudz) haploid cells resulting from meiosis

spermatocytes (spur-MA-tuh-syts) diploid cells contained within the seminiferous tubules that constantly undergo mitosis

spermatogenesis (spur-ma-tuh-JE-nuh-sus) in the male reproductive system, the point at which the male becomes sexually mature; in humans, this period is called *puberty.*

spermatozoa (spur-ma-tuh-ZOH-uh) male sex cell, or sperm

spinal cord (SPY-nul   KORD) the thick cord of nerve tissue which, in vertebrates, is protected by the backbone

spindle (SPIN-dul) the structure in cells that forms during reproduction; the chromosomes are distributed along the spindle, and they are drawn apart during both meiosis and mitosis.

spirilla (spy-RI-luh) spiral-shaped bacteria; the singular form is *spirillum.*

sponge (SPUNJ) a marine invertebrate that has cells, but no organs or systems

spongy bone (SPUN-jee   BOHN) bone tissue that contains pores, such as exists at the end of long bones

spontaneous generation (spon-TAY-nee-us   je-nuh-RAY-shun) the now-discredited notion that living organisms arose spontaneously from nonliving matter

spores (SPOHRZ) small reproductive bodies in some protists, fungi, and plants

stamen (STAY-mun) in flowers, the male reproductive structure

stapes (STAY-peez) one of the bones in the human inner ear; the smallest bone in the human body

---

PRONUNCIATION KEY

CAPITAL LETTERS show the stressed syllables.

a	as in m**a**t	f	as in **f**it	o	as in c**o**t, f**a**ther	uh	as in **a**bout, tak**e**n,
ay	as in d**ay**, s**ay**	g	as in **g**o	oh	as in g**o**, n**o**te		lem**o**n, penc**i**l
ch	as in **ch**ew	i	as in s**i**t	oo	as in t**oo**	ur	as in t**er**m
e	as in b**e**d	j	as in **j**ob, **g**em	sh	as in **sh**y	y	as in l**i**ne, fl**y**
ee	as in **e**ven, **ea**sy,	k	as in **c**ool, **k**ey	th	as in **th**in	zh	as in vi**s**ion,
	n**ee**d	ng	as in runni**ng**	u	as in b**u**t, s**o**me		mea**s**ure

start codon (START   KOH-don) the first codon in mRNA, beginning with the sequence AUG

stem (STEM) the part of a plant that provides support for leaves and that carries food and water through the plant

stem cells (STEM   SELZ) in the bone marrow, cells that divide constantly, creating red blood cells, white blood cells, and platelets

sternum (STUR-num) the bone over the chest, also called the breastbone

stigma (STIG-muh) part of a flower's female sex organs

stimuli (STIM-yuh-ly) the cause(s) of a response; the singular form is *stimulus.*

stomach (STUH-muk) large digestive organ, where food is partially digested

stomata (STOH-muh-tuh) in plants, small openings on the underside of leaves where gases are taken in and released; the singular form is *stoma.*

stop codon (STOP   KOH-don) the last codon in mRNA, ending with one of three sequences

stroke (STROHK) condition in which a major artery near the brain bursts, damaging a part of the brain

style (STYL) in plants, an extension of a flower's ovary, shaped like a stalk; supports the stigma

subcutaneous layer (sub-kyu-TAY-nee-us   LAY-ur) the inner layer of skin

substitution (sub-stuh-TOO-shun) a type of genetic mutation in which one nucleotide is substituted for another

succession (suk-SE-shun) the progression from grasses and fast-growing trees to shade-tolerant trees and plants in an ecosystem

succulent (SUH-kyuh-lunt) 1. a fleshy fruit; 2. a plant, such as a cactus, that retains water

sweat (SWET) a secretion performed by some mammals in which water and salts are excreted through glands at the surface of the skin; the water cools the skin and helps maintain the organism's body temperature.

sweat glands (SWET   GLANDZ) glands that excrete sweat

swim bladder (SWIM   BLA-dur) an organ in some fish used to control depth

symbiosis (sim-bee-OH-sus) a close relationship between two different organisms in which both organisms benefit from the association

symbiotic (sim-bee-O-tik) describing a condition of symbiosis

---

PRONUNCIATION KEY

CAPITAL LETTERS show the stressed syllables.

a as in m**a**t	f as in **f**it	o as in c**o**t, f**a**ther	uh as in **a**bout, tak**e**n, lem**o**n, penc**i**l
ay as in d**ay**, s**ay**	g as in **g**o	oh as in **g**o, n**o**te	
ch as in **ch**ew	i as in s**i**t	oo as in t**oo**	ur as in t**er**m
e as in b**e**d	j as in **j**ob, **g**em	sh as in **sh**y	y as in l**i**ne, fl**y**
ee as in **e**ven, **ea**sy, n**ee**d	k as in **c**ool, **k**ey	th as in **th**in	zh as in vi**s**ion, mea**s**ure
	ng as in runni**ng**	u as in b**u**t, s**o**me	

synaptic gap (suh-NAP-tik   GAP) in nerve cells, the space between axons and dendrites

synaptic knobs (suh-NAP-tik   NOBZ) in nerve cells, the structures at the ends of axons

synaptic vesicles (suh-NAP-tik   VE-si-kulz) in nerve cells, membrane-bound sacs found in the synaptic knobs that are filled with neurotransmitters

synovial fluid (suh-NOH-vee-ul   FLOO-ud) a greasy fluid found within membranes located at skeletal joints

synovial membrane (suh-NOH-vee-ul   MEM-brayn) a membrane found at skeletal joints that contains fluid

systolic pressure (sis-TO-lik   PRE-shur) the pressure of blood when the heart contracts

taiga (TY-guh) a zone of cold-weather forests, mostly evergreen

taproot (TAP-root) the large, main root of a plant that grows straight down

taste buds (TAYST   BUDZ) special chemical sensors on the surface of the tongue that can detect sourness, sweetness, saltiness, and bitterness

taxonomy (tak-SO-nuh-mee) the system used to classify living things

T-cells (TEE-SELZ) a special form of lymphocyte manufactured in the thymus that recognizes and destroys certain pathogens

telophase (TE-luh-fayz) the last phase of mitosis during which the chromosomes completely separate and the cell begins to fully divide

temporal lobe (TEM-prul   LOHB) in the human brain, one of two lobes containing the sensory centers responsible for hearing, some vision, and smell

tendons (TEN-dunz) collagen cords that anchor the muscle to the bone

tentacles (TEN-ti-kulz) long, flexible structures in some invertebrates that can grasp, sense, and sting

tertiary consumers (TER-shee-er-ee   kun-SOO-murz) organisms that consume secondary consumers

testes (TES-teez) male sexual organs, where sperm are produced

testosterone (te-STOS-tuh-rohn) the male sex hormone

thalamus (THA-luh-mus) in the human brain, the part of the brain that regulates sensory information

thermoreceptors (thur-moh-ri-SEP-turz) receptors in the skin that detect temperature

---

PRONUNCIATION KEY

CAPITAL LETTERS show the stressed syllables.

a	as in m**a**t	f	as in **f**it	o	as in c**o**t, f**a**ther	uh	as in **a**bout, tak**e**n,
ay	as in d**ay**, s**ay**	g	as in **g**o	oh	as in g**o**, n**o**te		lem**o**n, penc**i**l
ch	as in **ch**ew	i	as in s**i**t	oo	as in t**oo**	ur	as in t**er**m
e	as in b**e**d	j	as in **j**ob, **g**em	sh	as in **sh**y	y	as in l**i**ne, fl**y**
ee	as in **e**ven, **e**asy,	k	as in **c**ool, **k**ey	th	as in **th**in	zh	as in vi**s**ion,
	n**ee**d	ng	as in runni**ng**	u	as in b**u**t, s**o**me		mea**s**ure

Teacher's Guide • Biology

thoracic cavity (thuh-RA-sik KA-vuh-tee) the hollow area in the chest where organs such as the lungs can be found

thoracic duct (thuh-RA-sik DUKT) a large vein that empties out the lymph above the vena cava

thorax (THOHR-aks) the middle segment of an insect; contains the six legs and wings, if any

thymine (THY-meen) a component of nucleic acid that pairs with adenine in DNA

thyroid (THY-roid) a gland that produces hormones that control the metabolism

thyroid stimulating hormone (TSH) (THY-roid STIM-yuh-lay-ting HOR-mohn) (TEE-ES-AYCH) a hormone produced by the hypothalamus to stimulate the thyroid gland

thyroxin (thy-ROK-sun) the principal thyroid hormone; stimulates metabolism and is essential for growth and development

tongue (TUNG) the sensory organ responsible for discerning taste

toxin (TOK-sun) a poison

trachea (TRAY-kee-uh) a tube that carries air from the nose and mouth to the lungs; also called the windpipe

trait (TRAYT) visible expression of an organism's genetic code; for instance, blue eyes

transcription (tran-SKRIP-shun) the process by which mRNA is produced

transfer RNA (tRNA) (trans-FUR AR-EN-AY) type of RNA involved in protein synthesis

translation (trans-LAY-shun) the process by which RNA directs the sequence of amino acids assembled by a ribosome during protein synthesis

translocation (trans-loh-KAY-shun) the transfer of part of a chromosome to a new position on the same or a different chromosome, with a resulting rearrangement of the genes

transpiration (trans-puh-RAY-shun) in plants, the release of water through openings on the leaf surface

transport (TRANS-pohrt) the movement of fluids and nutrients around an organism's body

trimester (try-MES-tur) one of three periods of human pregnancy

tropical rain forests (TRO-pi-kul RAYN FOR-usts) rich biomes, with a great deal of diversity, that occur where the climate is warm all year round and where it rains almost every day

tropism (TROH-pi-zum) movement in response to a stimulus such as light or heat

tumor (TOO-mur) an abnormal mass of tissue

PRONUNCIATION KEY

CAPITAL LETTERS show the stressed syllables.

a	as in m**a**t	f	as in **f**it	o	as in c**o**t, f**a**ther	uh	as in **a**bout, tak**e**n, lem**o**n, penc**i**l
ay	as in d**ay**, s**ay**	g	as in **g**o	oh	as in g**o**, n**o**te		
ch	as in **ch**ew	i	as in s**i**t	oo	as in t**oo**	ur	as in t**er**m
e	as in b**e**d	j	as in **j**ob, **g**em	sh	as in **sh**y	y	as in l**i**ne, fl**y**
ee	as in **e**ven, **ea**sy, n**ee**d	k	as in **c**ool, **k**ey	th	as in **th**in	zh	as in vi**s**ion, mea**s**ure
		ng	as in runni**ng**	u	as in b**u**t, s**o**me		

tundra (TUN-druh) a cold, dry biome where few plants grow

tympanum (TIM-puh-num) a cavity in the middle ear also called the *eardrum*

unirames (yoo-nuh-RAYMZ) one of three subphyla within the phylum Arthropoda, which includes all insects, centipedes, and millipedes

uracil (YUR-uh-sil) a nitrogen base found in RNA nucleotides

urea (yu-REE-uh) a compound commonly found in mammal urine and in the decomposition process

ureters (YUR-uh-turz) tubes that transport urine from the kidneys to the bladder

urethra (yu-REE-thruh) tube through which urine is eliminated from the body

urine (UR-in) liquid that is removed from the body, along with impurities

uterus (YOO-tuh-rus) in female mammals, a hollow muscular organ in which the young develop

vacuoles (VA-kyuh-wohlz) storage chambers in cells that are used to hold nutrients and wastes

vagina (vuh-JY-nuh) in females, the passageway that leads from the uterus to the outside of the body

valves (VALVZ) 1. halves of a shell in a bivalve mollusk such as a clam; 2. flaps of tissue that open and close chambers in the heart

variation (ver-ee-AY-shun) a difference in coloration or other characteristic within the same species

vas deferens (VAS DE-fuh-runz) in males, the passageway through which sperm move from the testicles to the urethra

vascular plants (VAS-kyuh-lur PLANTS) plants with transport systems

vein (VAYN) 1. a vessel in plants that carries food and nutrients from roots to leaves and back; 2. a blood vessel that carries blood to the heart

ventricle (VEN-tri-kul) lower chamber of the human heart

venules (VEEN-yoolz) small veins that carry oxygen-poor blood back to the larger veins, which carry it back to the heart

vertebra (VUR-tuh-bruh) one of seven bones covering the spinal cord; the plural form is *vertebrae.*

vertebral column (vur-TEE-brul KO-lum) the spinal column

vertebrates (VER-te-brayts) animals with backbones

villi (VI-ly) fingerlike projections on the lining of the small intestine that absorb nutrients as food particles pass by; the singular form is *villus.*

PRONUNCIATION KEY

CAPITAL LETTERS show the stressed syllables.

a	as in m**a**t	f	as in **f**it	o	as in c**o**t, f**a**ther	uh	as in **a**bout, tak**e**n,
ay	as in d**ay**, s**ay**	g	as in **g**o	oh	as in g**o**, n**o**te		lem**o**n, penc**i**l
ch	as in **ch**ew	i	as in s**i**t	oo	as in t**oo**	ur	as in t**er**m
e	as in b**e**d	j	as in **j**ob, **g**em	sh	as in **sh**y	y	as in l**i**ne, fl**y**
ee	as in **e**ven, **ea**sy,	k	as in **c**ool, **k**ey	th	as in **th**in	zh	as in vi**s**ion,
	n**ee**d	ng	as in runni**ng**	u	as in b**u**t, s**o**me		mea**s**ure

virus (VY-rus) small, disease-causing particles that contain RNA or DNA but do not meet the criteria of living organisms

visceral mass (VI-suh-rul   MAS) in mollusks, the area containing the organs

vitreous humor (VI-tree-us   HYOO-mur) the clear gel that fills the eyeballs of mammals

vocal cords (VOH-kul   KORDZ) two ligaments that stretch over the larynx and produce sound when air passes over them

warmblooded (WARM-BLUH-dud) any organism that maintains a stable body temperature

water-soluble (WO-tur   SOL-yuh-bul) capable of being dissolved in water; vitamin C, for instance, is water-soluble.

white blood cells (HWYT   BLUD   SELZ) part of the body's defense system that surround pathogens and consume them

worm (WURM) one of many kinds of long, soft-bodied invertebrates

xylem (ZY-lum) plant tissue that carries water from the roots to the leaves

zygote (ZY-goht) a fertilized egg that will develop into a multicellular organism

---

PRONUNCIATION KEY

CAPITAL LETTERS show the stressed syllables.

a as in mat	f as in fit	o as in cot, father	uh as in about, taken,
ay as in day, say	g as in go	oh as in go, note	lemon, pencil
ch as in chew	i as in sit	oo as in too	ur as in term
e as in bed	j as in job, gem	sh as in shy	y as in line, fly
ee as in even, easy, need	k as in cool, key	th as in thin	zh as in vision,
	ng as in running	u as in but, some	measure

Teacher's Guide • Biology